SONGBOOK

OF THE

AMERICAN
REVOLUTION

THE NEW *MASSACHUSETTS*
LIBERTY SONG,

[*To the Tune of the* British Grenadier.]

I.

THAT Seat of Science ATHENS, and Earth's great Miſtreſs ROME,
  Where now are all their Glories, we ſcarce can find their Tomb :
Then guard your Rights, AMERICANS ! nor ſtoop to lawleſs Sway,
Oppoſe, oppoſe, oppoſe, oppoſe,----my brave AMERICA.

II.

Proud ALBION bow'd to *Cæſar*, and num'rous *Lords* before,
To *Piɛts*, to *Danes*, to *Normans*, and many Maſters more :
But we can boaſt AMERICANS ! we never fell a Prey ;
Huzza, huzza, huzza, huzza, for brave AMERICA.

III.

We led fair FREEDOM hither, when lo the *Deſart* ſmil'd,
A Paradiſe of Pleaſure, was open'd in the Wild ;
Your Harveſt bold AMERICANS ! no Power ſhall ſnatch away,
Aſſert yourſelves, yourſelves, yourſelves, my brave AMERICA.

IV.

Torn from a World of Tyrants, beneath this weſtern Sky,
We form'd a new Dominion, a *Land* of LIBERTY ;
The World ſhall own their Maſters here, then haſten on the Day,
Huzza, huzza, huzza, huzza, for brave AMERICA.

V.

GOD bleſs this maiden Climate, and thro' her vaſt Domain,
Let Hoſts of Heroes cluſter, who ſcorn to wear a Chain :
And blaſt the venal Sycophant, who dares our Rights betray,
Preſerve, preſerve, preſerve, preſerve my brave AMERICA.

VI.

Lift up your Heads my Heroes ! and ſwear with proud Diſdain,
The Wretch who would enſlave you, ſhall ſpread his Snares in vain ;
Should EUROPE empty all her Force, wou'd meet them in Array,
And ſhout, and ſhout, and ſhout, and ſhout, for brave AMERICA.

VII.

Some future Day ſhall crown us, the Maſters of the Main,
And giving Laws and Freedom, to ſubjeɛt FRANCE and SPAIN ;
When all the ISLES o'er Ocean ſpread, ſhall tremble and obey,
Their Lords, their Lords, their Lords, their Lords of brave AMERICA.

THE NEW MASSACHUSETTS LIBERTY SONG. Broadside; Boston, 1770.
Courtesy, The Historical Society of Pennsylvania. The tune, "The British
Grenadiers", is on p. 22.

SONGBOOK

OF THE

AMERICAN REVOLUTION

By

CAROLYN RABSON

With Illustrations By **NANCY HANSEN**

NEO Press, Box 32, Peaks Island, Maine 04108

© NEO Press 1974

Library of Congress Catalog Card Number 73-81353

International Standard Book Numbers   0-911014-18-7 (paperback)
0-911014-19-5 (hardcover)

ACKNOWLEDGMENTS

I wish to acknowledge the help of many people who contributed in various ways to the completion of this songbook.

First, I am greatly indebted to Dr. Irene Schensted, whose enthusiastic participation in the musicological research brought forth some of the best songs in the collection. For their capable and generous assistance to Dr. Schensted, I am grateful to Natalie Breed and Ruth Bleeker of the Boston Public Library, to the staffs of the Widener and Houghton Libraries of Harvard University, the Massachusetts Historical Society, the Portland Public Library, the Music and General Libraries of the University of Michigan, as well as to Howard Peckham, Director of the Clements Library, and to Gene Wilson, Head of the Reference Department of the Ann Arbor Public Library.

In addition, I wish to thank Dr. Alexander Hyatt King of the British Museum Music Room, Nicholas B. Wainwright of the Historical Society of Pennsylvania, Mrs. Georgia B. Bumgardner and Mrs. Carolyn Allen of the American Antiquarian Society for making available to me copies of original songsheets and broadsides, and for permission to use some of these materials in the songbook. I also would like to acknowledge the assistance of the Special Collections staff at the Music Division of the New York Public Library.

For their generous assistance and expertise, I wish to thank the following members of the staff at the Frederick W. Crumb Memorial Library at the State University of New York, College at Potsdam: Shirley Maul, Edith Frankel, Carol Wolstenholme, Peggy Overfield, Selma Foster, Nancy Lufborrow, Jeanne Dittmar, Violette Cotellessa, Frances Chilson, Alice Kauffman, Chris Gulick, Judith Hudson, Elinore Vorse, Alan Greenberg and David Trithart. I would also like to thank Dr. Perry H. Yaw of the Crane School of Music, Professor James H. Levitt of the History Department, Miss Sally Skyrm, Dr. David Ossenkop, Mrs. Barbara Lantry and Mrs. Anna Wilcox of the Julia E. Crane Music Library, at the State University of New York, College at Potsdam.

Additionally, I wish to express my gratitude to Nancy Hansen for her fine illustrations, and to Craige Schensted for his hand-lettered titles, which so greatly enhance the style of the songbook. Also, I want to thank Dr. Gustave Rabson for his assistance in the harmonic interpretation of the ballads and for proofing the music manuscripts. And for their various contributions, I would like to thank the following people: Sylvia

Angus, Douglas Angus, Marcia Barrabbee, Kay Bowers, Eugene Collins, Elizabeth Converse, Carolyn Funes, Donald Funes, Walter Kreske, Joanna Marston, Miriam Rabson, Jacqueline Turchek, Mary Verona, Rose Wilson and Scott Wilson.

C.R.

TABLE OF CONTENTS

Acknowledgments (i-ii)

Introduction (1-4)

Ballads (5-67)

* Tune selected for this song by C.R.

TABLE OF CONTENTS

* Tune selected for this song by C. R.

iv

TABLE OF CONTENTS

* Tune selected for this song by C.R.

INTRODUCTION

MODERN Americans have access to quantities of literary and visual material on every aspect of the American Revolution. THE SONGBOOK OF THE AMERICAN REVOLUTION presents another means of evoking the flavor of the era -- through the dimension of sound. These are the tunes that were current in the colonies at the time of the Revolution; the verses are authentic statements of prevalent attitudes during the war years. We hope that the songs will provide the reader with historical atmosphere and insight as well as with many pleasant hours of music.

The Ballads

THE first and largest section contains a selection of political ballads written by the colonists during the American Revolution and the years just preceding the outbreak of hostilities. American colonists from every walk of life were moved to poetic commentary, however unpolished at times, by the developing events of those troubled years. The frankly partisan verses were set to well-known tunes of the day, and could be quickly learned, savored and passed on from one sympathizer to another. At a time when methods of communication were severely limited and a large part of the general population was barely literate, the political ballad was unexcelled as a vehicle for factional propaganda.

Ballads could accomplish many purposes. They stirred patriotic feel-ing to new heights, strengthened the determination to resist, spread news of current events in the "proper" perspective, capitalized on humiliations suffered by the enemy, or simply indulged in pure, malicious invective. Naturally, opposing factions counterattacked in kind. Thus, a lively exchange of ballad-fire between the colonial rebels (Whigs) and colonial loyalists (Tories) was maintained throughout the war.

It should be remembered that these public volleys in verse were an accepted feature of eighteenth-century English life, and a natural part of the British subject's cultural heritage, whether at home or in the colonies. Origins of the custom can be found in the methods of itinerant ballad-singers who stood on London street corners, singing the latest news and gossip to well-known tunes and selling printed copies of the verses. Techniques of the street-singers gradually crept onto the English stage. Ben Jonson, Thomas D'Urfey and other English poets incorporated original verses, sung to familiar tunes, into their plays. In John Gay's BEGGAR'S OPERA, first produced in London in 1728, cleverly versified attacks on government officials, and cynical commentaries on English social institutions in general, were set to simple folk tunes.

The immense popularity of the BEGGAR'S OPERA, and later ballad-operas, made the ballad habit a part of daily life in England. Every citizen had a means of expressing his opinion,

1

while maintaining his anonymity, by composing new verses to an old tune and publishing them in newspapers, magazines or single ballad-sheets. The following example, lamenting the decline of Italian opera in England as a result of the popular ballad-operas, illustrates the standard format:

Old England's Garland; or The Italian Opera's Downfall.
    An excellent new ballad, to the tune of
    King John and the Abbot of Canterbury...

I sing of sad discords that happened of late,
Of strange revolutions, but not in the state;
How Old England grew fond of old tunes of her own,
And her ballads went up and our operas down,
    Derry down, down, hey, derry down. *

Many examples of ballads written in eighteenth-century America are to be found in the poetry columns of surviving colonial newspapers and magazines, or on single-sheet broadsides which were sold on the streets of colonial cities. Political ballads from these sources have been gathered together in two collections by nineteenth-century American historians: Winthrop Sargent's LOYALIST POETRY OF THE REVOLUTION (1857), and Frank Moore's SONGS AND BALLADS OF THE AMERICAN REVOLUTION (1855). In addition to material from printed sources, Frank Moore's collection includes a few songs preserved through the oral tradition.

Colonial ballads followed the standard English format, giving the verses but no music. Even the tune to be used was not always indicated. The fact that these provocative verses appear without a single note of music, in the

* Quoted by Chappell in Ballad Literature, Vol. II, p. 630, from Miscellaneous Poems by Several Hands, London: D. Lewis, 1730. The tune for the ballad quoted here will be found on p. 15 of this songbook.

original sources as well as the later collections, probably best explains their relegation to near oblivion in the national memory. In this songbook, we have attempted to restore the original tunes to the ballads, insofar as possible, and to present the verses and music together in a format designed to encourage performance.

The majority of ballad tunes presented in this edition were indicated by name only in the broadsides or periodicals where the verses were first published, or in the later collections of Moore and Sargent. The tunes have been unearthed from a variety of sources including song collections and instrumental arrangements of popular tunes published in America during the eighteenth century, English and Scottish magazines and song collections of the eighteenth and nineteenth centuries, and English ballad-operas of the early eighteenth century. William Chappell's BALLAD LITERATURE AND POPULAR MUSIC OF THE OLDEN TIME (1859) and Claude M. Simpson's THE BRITISH BROADSIDE BALLAD AND ITS MUSIC (1966) are particularly valuable guides to the tunes and their histories.

Since the given titles of the tunes are often associated with more than one melody, and the melodies themselves are subject to variation, a process of tune selection was required for this book. The three criteria for tune selection used by the author were: (1) the fit of the verses to the tune, and their similarity to previous verses written to the same tune; (2) the proximity of date and place of the tune-source's publication to the Revolution; and (3) suitability of the melody to the sentiment of the verses. The author's intentions in the selection process are well expressed in the following excerpt from the preface to the AMERICAN MUSICAL MISCELLANY (1798):

The Editors...present the public with the following collection of Songs, accompanied with Notes: -- and whenever they have found the same words of a song sung in different tunes, (which is not unfrequently the case) they have endeavored to select such notes as, in their opinion, were best adapted to the words; but whether they have, in every instance, been happy in their selections, will be determined by the connoisseurs in the science of music...

A few ballads with no tune indicated in the source have been included in this collection, to preserve the continuity of ballad response to the most essential aspects of the war. They are set to tunes selected by the author from among the same sources that contain the tunes indicated for the other ballads in the book. Tunes thus selected by the author are indicated by * in the Table of Contents. Other relevant information concerning the reasons for the selection of tunes is included in the **Sources and Notes** Section on pp. 93-102.

The ballad tunes are presented as single-line melodies, to be sung either without accompaniment or with a guitar. In the case of certain tunes, the guitarist may wish to use a different harmonic interpretation from the one indicated by the guitar chords in this book. Most of the ballad tunes adapt nicely to instrumental performance on a fife or high recorder; many of them were marching tunes and can be performed with fife and drum.

The Hymns

OF all musical forms, the hymn is one of the most typically American.

The first 150 years of our musical history consists almost entirely of psalm-settings and hymn tunes. The association of religious and political causes is by no means unprecedented in human history. The issues of the Revolutionary period were aired in churches as well as in secular meeting places, and it was natural that at least some of the hymns composed during the war years would reflect the upheaval of worldly affairs.

The hymns are presented in this songbook in their four-part settings, as they are given in the sources. Piano reductions have been added only to facilitate rehearsals; the hymns should be performed without accompaniment. According to American hymn tradition, the melodies will be found in the tenor line; the harmonies do not necessarily conform to the rules of "common practice". The melodies may be sung alone, or played on a fife or other instrument, and may even be accompanied by appropriate drum beats.

The National Songs

THE songbook ends with a group of compositions selected from the patriotic outpourings of the postwar years, in which the heroes and ideals of the conflict are accorded an almost worshipful acclaim by jubilant citizens of the infant nation.

One of these songs is clearly in the ballad category, and two others incorporate familiar tunes in combination with newly composed sections. Only the last two can be called truly original compositions in both words and music.

All the National Songs are presented exactly as they are given in the original source. The sparse bass lines were clearly meant to be elaborated and they offer an interesting challenge to the creative modern keyboard player. The melodies are as suitable as the other songs in the book to be played on fifes or other instruments, with or without drums.

The Organization of the Songs

FOR convenience, the songs have been separated into the three categories described above -- Ballads, Hymns and National Songs, although familiarity with the contents will reveal some unavoidable overlapping of categories. Within each group, the songs are generally presented in chronological order. A departure from the chronological sequence occurs in the case of tunes with two or more sets of verses published at widely separated intervals during the war. In such cases, the earliest version is set to the tune and additional sets of verses are presented immediately afterward, rather than separating them from their tune by adherence to the over-all sequence. In order to help clarify the arrangement and facilitate use of the book, the dates of the songs are included in the Table of Contents.

Some verses have been omitted from several of the songs, either because of space limitations or indelicacy of content.

The Sources and Notes

THE sources of all the verses and tunes used in this songbook are listed in the **Sources And Notes** section on pp. 93-102 . Notes indicated by number in the text, as well as additional notes and comments about the music, and other relevant material, are all included with the source information on each song. The sequence of the **Sources And Notes** section coincides with the order of presentation in the book; items are listed by page number and title of the songs.

Thus, gentle Reader, you have my sentiments on the matter.

No doubt they're faulty, pray excuse 'em,
If you like 'em, prithee use 'em;
Critics, be Tender, don't abuse 'em.

William Billings
The New England Psalm Singer
Boston, 1770

Ballads

FOUR SONGS
TO THE TUNE
HEARTS OF OAK

THE popularity of the British sea-chanty "Hearts of Oak" in both England and the colonies is reflected in the large number of political ballads set to it by both sides during the American Revolution. Two of the four versions presented here express the Tory point of view and two the cause of the colonists.

THE

LIBERTY

SONG

THESE verses by John Dickinson of Delaware were published by the BOSTON GAZETTE in July of 1768. They urge unified resistance to England's taxation of the American colonies. The last verse indicates that the colonists were not yet thinking of complete independence from England.

6

COME join hand in hand, brave Americans all,
And rouse your bold hearts at fair Liberty's call;
No tyrannous acts shall suppress your just claim
Nor stain with dishonor America's name.
In freedom we're born and in freedom we'll live;
Our purses are ready, Steady, friends, steady,
Not as slaves but as freemen our money we'll give.

Our worthy forefathers -- let's give them a cheer --
To climates unknown did courageously steer;
Through oceans to deserts, for freedom they came,
And, dying, bequeathed us their freedom and fame.
In freedom we're born, &c.

How sweet are the labors that freemen endure,
That they shall enjoy all the profit, secure --
No more such sweet labors Americans know
If Britons shall reap what Americans sow.
In freedom we're born, &c.

Then join hand in hand brave Americans all,
By uniting we stand, by dividing we fall;
In so righteous a cause let us hope to succeed,
For Heaven approves of each generous deed.
In freedom we're born, &c.

This bumper I crown for our sovereign's health,
And this for Britannia's glory and wealth;
That wealth and that glory immortal may be,
If she is but just, and we are but free.
In freedom we're born, &c.

A PARODY ON A Liberty Song

THIS could be called a pre-Revolutionary law-and-order song. It was sent to the BOSTON GAZETTE in September of 1768 by an anonymous author "from a garret in Castle William." The Castle William, an island fortress in Massachusetts Bay which housed the British army troops stationed in Boston, was frequently sought as a refuge by British officials in times of crisis. During the riots that arose on June 10, 1768 when British customs seized one of John Hancock's ships, the mob of colonists became so violent that the commissioners of customs fled to the Castle William where they remained under British protection.

COME shake your dull noddles, ye pumpkins, and bawl,
And own you've gone mad at fair Liberty's call;
No scandalous conduct can add to your shame
Condemned to dishonor, inherit the fame.
In folly you're born and in folly you'll live
To madness still ready, stupidly steady,
Not as men, but as monkeys, the tokens you give.

Such villains, such rascals all dangers despise
And stick not at mobbing when mischief's the prize.
In defiance of halters, of whips and of chains,
The rogues would run riot, fools for their pains.
In folly you're born, &c.

Your Grandsire, Old Satan, now give him a cheer
Would act like yourselves and as wildly would steer.
But short is your harvest, nor long shall you know
The pleasure of reaping what other men sow.
In folly you're born, &c.

Then plunder, my lads, for when red-coats appear
You'll melt like the locust when winter is near.
Your cursed old trade of purloining must cease
The dread and the curse of all order and peace.
In folly you're born, &c.

Gulp down your last dram, for the gallows now groans
And, over depressed, her lost empire bemoans;
While we quite transported and happy shall be
From mobs, knaves and villains, protected and free.
In folly you're born, &c.

A NEW Liberty Song

DON'T TREAD ON ME

THESE verses were written in 1775 by J. W. Hewlings of Virginia. They clearly express the growing concept of union, and urge other colonies to join Massachusetts in her determined resistance to British authority.

COME rouse up my lads and join this great cause,
In defence of your liberty, your property and laws!
'Tis to honor we call you, stand up for your right,
And ne'er let our foes say, we are put to the flight.
For so just is our cause, and so valiant our men
We always are ready, steady boys, steady;
We'll fight for our freedom again and again.

The placemen and commoners have taken a bribe
To betray their own country, and the empire beside;
And though the colonies stand condemned by some,
There are no rebels here, but are traitors at home.
For so just is our cause, &c.

They tax us contrary to reason and right,
Expecting that we are not able to fight;
But to draw their troop home, I do think would be best,
For Providence always defends the oppressed.
For so just is our cause, &c.

The valiant Bostonians have entered the field,
And declare they will fall there before they will yield:
A noble example! In them we'll confide,
We'll march to their town, stand or fall by their side.
For so just is our cause, &c.

And union through the colonies will ever remain,
And ministerial taxation will be but in vain,
For we are all resolved to die or be free;
So they may repeal the acts, for repealed they must be.
For so just is our cause, &c.

A REFUGEE SONG

THE war was well under way when this song was written in 1779. By this time, the Continental Army had succeeded in driving the British out of the occupied cities of Boston and Philadelphia, and many colonial loyalists had fled with the retreating British Armies to Nova Scotia and New York. These verses were first sung at the Refugee Club in New York; the author expresses his steadfast devotion to the British Crown.

HERE'S a bumper, brave boys, to the health of our king,
Long may he live, and long may we sing,
In praise of a monarch who boldly defends
The laws of the realm, and the cause of his friends.
Then cheer up, my lads, we have nothing to fear,
While we remain steady and always keep ready
To add to the trophies of this happy year.

The Congress did boast of their mighty ally,
But George does both France and the Congress defy;
And when Britons unite, there's no force can withstand
Their fleets and their armies, by sea and on land.
Then cheer up, &c.

Thus supported, our cause we will ever maintain,
And all treaties with rebels will ever disdain;
Till reduced by our arms, they are forced to confess,
While ruled by Great Britain they ne'er knew distress.
Then cheer up, &c.

Then let us, my boys, Britain's right e'er defend,
Who regards not her rights, we esteem not our friend;
Then, brave boys, we both France and the Congress defy,
And we'll fight for Great Britain and George 'til we die.
Then cheer up, &c.

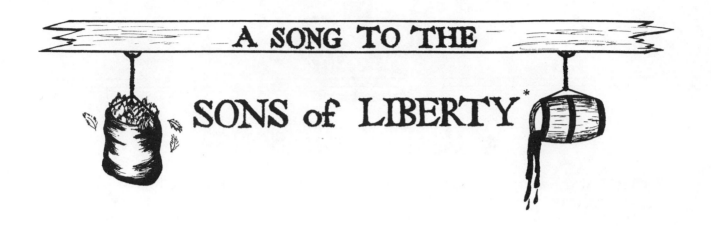

A SONG TO THE SONS of LIBERTY*

Tune: COME, JOLLY BACCHUS

THE nucleus of colonial resistance, before the Revolution, was an organization called the Sons of Liberty. Their activities, ranging from propaganda and petitions to rallies and riots, ensured a continuous demonstration of popular support for the formal statements of protest drawn up by colonial assemblies.

This song was written for an elaborate celebration held in 1768, commemorating the Stamp Act riots of August 14, 1765.[1] The festivities served as a pep-rally, launching the boycott of British goods by Boston merchants.

Come jol-ly Sons of Lib-er-ty, Come all with hearts u-nit-ed.

Our mot-to is "We dare be free," Not ea-si-ly af-fright-ed. Op-

pres-sion's bond we must sub-due, Now is the time or nev - - er;

Let each man prove this Mot-to true And slav-er-y from him sev - er.

*Illustration by C.R.

COME jolly Sons of Liberty
Come all with hearts united.
Our Motto is "We dare be free",
Not easily affrighted!
Oppression's bond we must subdue,
Now is the time or never;
Let each man prove this motto true
And slavery from him sever.

Pale vissag'd Fear, let none possess!
Or Terrors e're perplex him,
Posterity will ever bless,
And nought hereafter vex him;
To Freedom's Banner, let's repair,
When e're we see Occasion ...
Nor wives nor Children, tho' most dear,
E're stop to look or gaze on.

In Freedom's Cause, the slavish Knave,
'Twere better his Condition
(That might his Country's Ruin save!)
To sink into Perdition;
Chain'd to a Galley, groan his days,
And never be forgotten,
While Furies croak his Bondage Lays
After he's dead and Rotten.

See Liberty high poiz'd in Air
Her Free Born Sons commanding,
"Come on, my Sons, without a fear,
"Your Nat'ral Rights demanding!
"Your Cause, the Gods proclaim is Just
"Can tamely, you, be fetter'd?
"In which, disturb your Father's Dust!
"With 'S', be ever letter'd!"

Obey, my brothers, Nature's call
Your country too demands it!
Let Liberty ne'er have a Fall!
'Tis Freedom that commands it.
The Ax, now to the Root is laid.
Will you be Bond or Free?
No time to pause -- then "Whose afraid?"
Live or die in Liberty!

13

FOUR SONGS
TO THE TUNE
DERRY DOWN

ANOTHER popular English tune that was frequently used as a setting for new ballad verses was DERRY DOWN. Only four of the many versions from the American Revolutionary period are presented here.

CASTLE ISLAND SONG

THIS song expresses the resentment of the British troops upon being ordered to withdraw from their billets in Boston and to return to their former barracks in Castle William. The orders were issued as a conciliatory gesture toward Bostonians who were in a violent mood after the incident which came to be known as "the Boston Massacre". On March 5, 1770, a quarrel arose between two British soldiers and several Bostonian workmen. Both sides drew reinforcements and the level of hostilities grew. When British soldiers mistook a shout from the crowd for an order to fire, four citizens were killed and several others were injured. The Boston rebels made the most of this event to further their cause among colonial fence-sitters.

The Liberty Tree was originally a large elm that grew on High Street in Boston. Throughout the excitement in pre-Revolutionary Boston, this tree was the traditional scene of rebel propaganda and Tory humiliation. Liberty trees were consecrated in several other colonial towns.

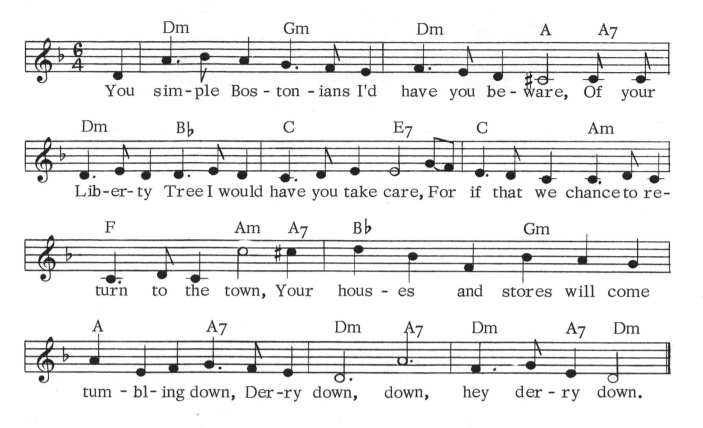

YOU simple Bostonians, I'd have you beware
Of your Liberty Tree, I would have you take care,
For if that we chance to return to the town,
Your houses and stores will come tumbling down.
Derry down, down, hey derry down.

If you will not agree to Old England's laws,
I fear that King Hancock will soon get the yaws;
But he need not fear, for I swear we will,
For the want of a doctor give him a hard pill.
Derry down, down, hey derry down.

A brave reinforcement, we soon think to get;
Then we will make you poor pumpkins to sweat.
Our drums they'll rattle, and then you will run
To the devil himself, from the sight of a gun.
Derry down, down, hey derry down.

Our fleet and our army, they soon will arrive,
Then to a bleak island, you shall not us drive.
In every house, you shall have three or four,
And if that will not please you, you'll have half a score.
Derry down, down, hey derry down.

A NEW SONG TO AN OLD TUNE

THIS ballad of 1775 expresses the colonists' growing resentment of repressive measures enacted by Parliament in reprisal for the Boston Tea Party and other colonial resistance activities. The port of Boston was closed to all trade that was not required to maintain the occupying British army; waters available to New England fishermen were severely limited. The city of Boston was virtually in a state of siege and Bostonians were suffering severe deprivation.

The names listed in the first verse refer to six members of Parliament who were outspoken champions of American colonial rights. The three British generals mentioned in the fourth verse were Howe, Clinton and Burgoyne, who had just arrived with a large contingent of fresh troops to see that the acts were enforced.

The Liberty Tree continued to be a symbol of colonial resistance, in this and other songs and verses written throughout the war years, even though the British had cut down Boston's original Liberty Tree in 1774.

WHAT a court hath Old England, of folly and sin,
　　Spite of Chatham, and Camden, Barre, Burke,
Wilkes and Glynn.
Not content with the game act they tax fish and sea.
And America drench with hot water and tea.
Derry down, down, hey derry down.

But if the wise council of England doth think
They may be enslaved by the power of drink
They're right to enforce it; but then do you see?
The Colonies, too, may refuse and be free.
Derry down, down, hey derry down.

There's no knowing where this oppression will stop;
Some say there's no cure but a capital chop;
And that I believe's each American's wish.
Since you've drenched them with tea, and deprived
　　'em of fish.
Derry down, down, hey derry down.

Three generals these mandates have borne 'cross
  the sea,
To deprive 'em of fish and to make ' em drink tea;
In turn, sure, these freemen will boldly agree,
To give 'em a dance upon Liberty Tree,
Derry down, down, hey derry down.

Then **Freedom's** the word, both at home and abroad,
And .... every scabbard that hides a good sword!
Our forefathers gave us this freedom in hand,
And we' ll die in defence of the rights of the land.
Derry down, down, hey derry down.

The PUBLIC SPIRIT of the WOMEN

ONE of the greatest advantages possessed by the rebel colonists was the unflinching support of their women. From the earliest boycotts of taxed English goods to the harvest of crops sown in the absence of farmer-soldiers, the rebel women met every hardship with a staunch spirit of dedication.

Their invaluable contributions to the war effort were recognized in many verses and songs. This one comes from a man in his seventies, who presumably stayed behind with the women and had a chance to see them in action.

THOUGH age at my elbow has taken his stand,
  And Time has stretch'd o'er me his wrinkling hand;
Our patriot fair like a charm can inspire,
In three-score-and-ten, twenty's spirit and fire.
Derry down, down, hey derry down.

Boy, fill me a bumper! as long as I live,
The patriot fair for my toast must I give;
Here' s a health to the sex of every degree,
Where sweetness and beauty with firmness agree.
Derry down, down, hey derry down.

No more will I babble of times that are past,
My wish is, the present forever may last;
Already I see sulky George in despair,
Should he vanquish the men, to vanquish the fair.
Derry down, down, hey derry down.

Could time be roll'd backward, and age become young,
My heart swell with ardor, my arm be new strung;
Under Washington's banner I'd cheerfully fight,
Where the smiles of the fair with glory unite.
Derry down, down, hey derry down.

Fill a bumper again, boy, and let it go round,
For the waters of youth in claret are found;
The younkers shall know, I've the courage to dare
Drink as deep as the best to the patriot fair.
Derry down, down, hey derry down.

The EPILOGUE

THESE verses were written early in 1778 while Philadelphia was occupied by the British army. The traditional importance attached to the conquest of the enemy capital was unfounded in this case, since the Congress simply moved to Yorktown, Virginia, and continued its sessions uninterrupted, while Washington's unharmed army waited and watched.

Nevertheless, Loyalists hailed the arrival of British troops as signalling the end of the rebel cause. In a some-what forced metaphor the author of this song refers to the American rebellion as "An admirable farce called INDEPENDENCE." Its epilogue is delivered by the rebel jester in Shakespearean style. The jester admits that the plot did not turn out quite as the rebel actors had intended, and suggests their renewed allegiance to the king and reconciliation with loyal colonists, rather than mis-alliance with the French.

OUR farce is now finish'd, your sport's at an end,
But ere you depart, let the voice of a friend
By way of a chorus, the evening crown
With a song to the tune of a hey derry down.
Derry down, down, hey derry down.

On this puny stage we've strutted our hour,
And have acted our parts to the best of our power;
That a farce hath concluded not perfectly well,
Was surely the fault of the devil in hell.
Derry down, down, hey derry down.

Since this is the case, we must e'en make the best
Of a game that is lost; let us turn it to jest;
We'll smile, nay, we'll laugh, we'll carouse and we'll sing,
And cheerfully drink life and health to the king.
Derry down, down, hey derry down.

Let Washington now from his mountains descend,
Who knows but in George he may still find a friend;
A Briton, altho' he loves bottle and wench,
Is an honester fellow than parle vous French.
Derry down, down, hey derry down.

Our great Independence we give to the wind,
And pray that Great Britain may once more be kind.
In this jovial song all hostility ends,
And Britons and we will forever be friends.
Derry down, down, hey derry down.

Good night! my good people, retire to your houses,
Fair ladies, I beg you, convince your dear spouses
That Britons and we are united in bliss,
And ratify all with a conjugal kiss.
Derry down, down, hey derry down.

Once more, here's a health to the King and Queen!
Confusion to him, who in rancor and spleen,
Refuses to drink with an English friend,
Immutable amity to the world's end.
Derry down, down, hey derry down.

A TEA PARTY SONG

Tune: HOSIER'S GHOST

THIS is one of many songs describing that important and complex event in our history known as "The Boston Tea Party". In 1773, England enacted new economic measures with the purpose of saving the foundering East India Tea Company, a commercial colossus which dominated the British economy of the eighteenth century. The success of the plan depended primarily upon exploitation of the huge tea market in the American colonies. Although the new measures included a lower price for tea, the colonists feared that they would lead to a British monopoly, first on the tea trade and then on other commodities. The colonists united in their resolve to continue their boycott of taxed British products, vowing that they would prevent the tea from touching American soil.

The now-famous confrontation occurred in November of 1773 when three tea-ships came to anchor in Boston harbor. Once within the harbor, no ship could leave without permission from the Royal Governor. This would be granted by Governor Hutchinson only after he received the required papers from customs stating that the cargo had been unloaded and all duties paid on it.

Since the Bostonians would not permit the tea to be landed, the resulting impasse might have continued indefinitely but for the regulation requiring customs to seize any cargo on which duty remained unpaid after twenty days in port. On the eve of the twentieth day, news was received of the governor's refusal to issue a sailing permit. Then a group of the Sons of Liberty in Indian disguise boarded the ships, opened the chests of tea, and threw the contents overboard.

Nothing in the colonists' previous behavior had prepared the British leaders for this. "In the British view of the time, to hang the governor in effigy or tar and feather a customs officer could be thought of as mere exuberance; but to destroy valuable property was to call into question the fundamentals of society."[1]

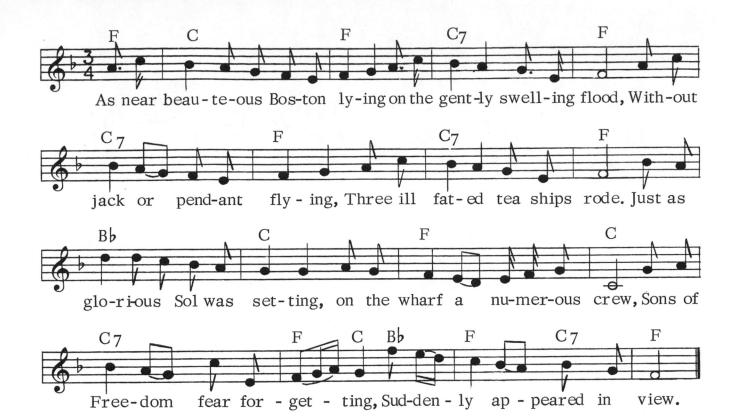

As near beauteous Boston lying
On the gently swelling flood,
Without jack or pendant flying
Three ill-fated tea ships rode.
Just as glorious Sol was setting,
On the wharf a numerous crew
Sons of Freedom, fear forgetting
Suddenly appeared in view.

Armed with hammers, axe and chisels
Weapons new for warlike deed,
Towards the herbage-freighted vessels,
They approached with dreadful speed.
Quick as thought the ships were boarded,
Hatches burst and chests displayed;
Axes, hammers help afforded;
What a glorious crash they made.

Squash into the deep descended
Cursed weed of China's coast;
Thus at once our fears were ended;
British rights shall ne'er be lost.
Captains! Once more hoist your streamers
Spread your sails, and plough the wave,
Tell your masters they were dreamers,
When they thought to cheat the brave.

A SONG ON LIBERTY

Tune: BRITISH GRENADIERS

IN 1774, when this song first appeared, the city of Boston was occupied by British troops and the port was closed in reprisal for the Boston Tea Party. Boston patriots hoped to convince the other colonies to join Massachusetts in opposition to the British. The verses have been attributed to the prominent Bostonian, Joseph Warren, who was killed in the battle of Bunker Hill only a year after the song was published.

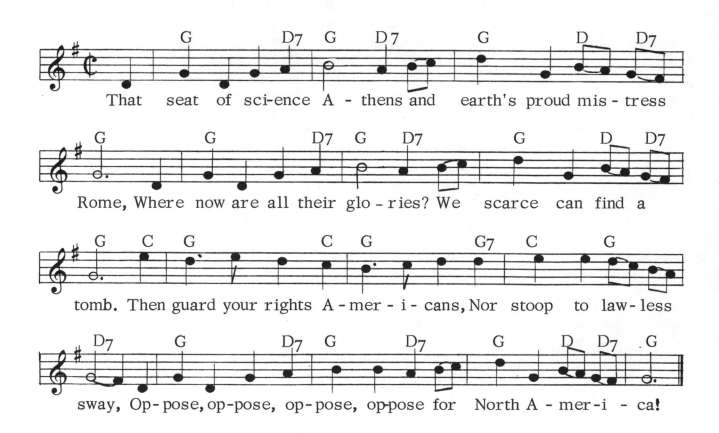

That seat of sci-ence A - thens and earth's proud mis - tress Rome, Where now are all their glo - ries? We scarce can find a tomb. Then guard your rights A - mer - i - cans, Nor stoop to law - less sway, Op-pose, op-pose, op-pose, op-pose for North A - mer - i - ca!

THAT seat of science Athens,
And earth's proud mistress, Rome,
Where now are all their glories?
We scarce can find a tomb.
Then guard your rights, Americans,
Nor stoop to lawless sway,
Oppose, oppose, oppose, oppose
For North America.

Proud Albion bow'd to Caesar,
And numerous lords before,
To Picts, to Danes, to Normans,
And many masters more;
But we can boast Americans
Have never fall'n a prey,
Huzza, huzza, huzza, huzza
For Free America.

We led fair Freedom hither,
And lo, the desert smiled,
A paradise of pleasure
New opened in the wild;
Your harvest, bold Americans,
No power shall snatch away,
Preserve, preserve, preserve
    your rights
In Free America.

Torn from a world of tyrants,
Beneath this western sky,
We formed a new dominion,
A land of liberty;
The world shall own we're freemen
    here,
And such will ever be,
Huzza, huzza, huzza, huzza
For love and liberty.

God bless this maiden climate,
And through her vast domain
May hosts of heroes cluster
That scorn to wear a chain.
And blast the venal sycophants
Who dare our rights betray;
Assert yourselves, yourselves, yourselves
For brave America.

Lift up your hearts, my heroes,
And swear with proud disdain,
The wretch that would ensnare you
Shall spread his net in vain;
Should Europe empty all her force,
We'd meet them in array,
And shout huzza, huzza, huzza
For brave America.

The land where freedom reigns
    shall still
Be masters of the main,
In giving laws and freedom
To subject France and Spain;
And all the isles o'er ocean spread
Shall tremble and obey,
The prince who rules by freedom's laws
In North America.

The WHIG *

Tune: POOR ROBIN'S MAGGOT

AS the rebel cause gained momentum, life became increasingly uncomfortable for the colonists who remained loyal to the crown. They were subjected to a variety of indignities, from verbal threats to tar-and-feathers, at the hands of their rebellious neighbors.

The two opposing groups of American colonists applied the traditional labels of English politics to each other: Loyalists were called Tories, and Rebels became Whigs. This song states the Tory view of the Whig as a symbol of lawlessness and evil. It is not clear from the source whether the verses originated in the colonies during the Revolution, or were adapted as appropriate from an earlier political situation in England.

Would you know what a Whig is and al-ways was? I'll show you his face as it were in a glass, He's a re-bel by na-ture a vil-lain in grain, A saint by pro-fes-sion who ne-ver had grace. Cheat-ing and ly-ing are pu-ny things; Ra-pine and plun-der-ing ve-nial sins; His great oc-cu-pa-tion is ru-in-ing na-tions, Sub-vert-ing of Crowns and mur-der-ing Kings.

*Tar and Feathers by C.R.

WOULD you know what a Whig is and always was?
I'll show you his face as it were in a glass
He's a rebel by nature, a villain in grain,
A saint by profession who never had grace.
Cheating and lying are puny things;
Rapine and plundering venial sins;
His great occupation is ruining nations,
Subverting of Crowns, and murdering Kings.

To show that he came from a wight of worth
'Twas Lucifer's pride that first gave him birth:
'Twas bloody Barbarity bore the elf:
Ambition the midwife that brought him forth.
Old Judas was tutor, until he grew big;
Hypocrisy taught him to care not a fig
For all that is sacred, -- and thus was created
And brought in the world, what we call a Whig.

Spewed up among mortals by hellish jaws,
To strike he begins at religion and laws;
With pious inventions and bloody intentions,
And all for to bring in the good of the cause.
At cheating and lying he plays his game;
Always dissembling, and never the same;
Till he fills the whole nation with sins of d-n-t-n
Then goes to the d-v-l, from whence he came!

The Banks of the Dee

Tune: LANGOLEE

THE BANKS OF THE DEE was written in 1775 by the Scottish poet John Tait when a close friend went off as a mercenary soldier to put down the rebellion in Britain's American colonies. The song became popular in the colonies as well as in England.

A PARODY ON THE BANKS OF THE DEE is attributed to Oliver Arnold of Norwich, Connecticut, who was known for his wit and for his political verses during the Revolution. In the verses of the parody, he cleverly reprimands the Scottish soldiers for siding with Britain, and, in the apt pun of the last verse, he suggests that restoration of England's tottering economy might well be achieved by taxing Scotland rather than the American colonies.

'TWAS summer, and softly the breezes were blowing
And sweetly the wood-pigeon cooed from the tree.
At the foot of a hill, where the river was flowing,
I sat myself down on the banks of the Dee.
Flow on lovely Dee, flow on thou sweet river,
Thy banks, purest stream, shall be dear to me ever,
For there I first gained the affection and favor
Of Jamie, the glory and pride of the Dee.

But now he's gone from me, and left me thus mourning.
To quell the proud rebels, for valiant is he;
But ah! there's no hope of his speedy returning,
To wander again on the banks of the Dee:
He's gone, hapless youth, o'er the rude roaring billows,
The kindest, the sweetest, of all his brave fellows;
And left me to stray 'mongst these once loved willows,
The loneliest lass on the banks of the Dee.

But time and my prayers may perhaps yet restore him,
Blest peace may restore my dear lover to me,
And when he returns, with such care I'll watch o'er him,
He never shall leave the sweet banks of the Dee.
The Dee will then flow, all its beauty displaying,
The lambs on its banks will again be seen playing,
Whilst I, with my Jamie, am carelessly straying,
And tasting again all the sweets of the Dee.

A PARODY ON
The Banks of the Dee

'Twas win-ter and blue To-ry nos-es were freez-ing As they marched o'er the land where they ought not to be. The val-iants com-plained at the fi-fers' cursed wheez-ing and wished they'd re-mained on the banks of the Dee. Lead on thou paid cap-tain! tramp on thou proud min-ions! Thy ranks, bas-est men, shall be strung like ripe on-ions, For here thou hast found heads with war-like o-pin-ions, On the shoul-ders of no-bles who ne'er saw the Dee.

A PARODY ON
The Banks of the Dee

'TWAS winter,and blue Tory noses were freezing,
   As they marched o'er the land where they ought not to be.
The valiants complained at the fifers' cursed wheezing,
And wished they'd remained on the banks of the Dee.
Lead on thou paid captain! tramp on thou proud minions!
Thy ranks, basest men, shall be strung like ripe onions,
For here thou hast found heads with warlike opinions
On the shoulders of nobles who ne'er saw the Dee.

Prepare for war's conflict; or make preparation
For peace with the rebels, for they're brave and glee;
Keep mindful of dying, and leave the foul nation
That sends out its armies to brag and to flee.
Make haste, now, and leave us thou miscreant Tories!
To Scotland repair! there court the sad houris,
And listen once more to their plaints and their stories
Concerning the "glory and pride of the Dee."

Be quiet and sober, secure and contented;
Upon your own land, be valiant and free;
Bless God, that the war is so nicely prevented,
And till the green fields on the banks of the Dee.
The Dee then will flow, all its beauty displaying,
The lads on its banks will again be seen playing
And England thus honestly taxes defraying
With natural drafts from the banks of the Dee.

A JUNTO SONG

Tune: A-BEGGING WE WILL GO

Instead of subduing rebellion, the blockade of the Boston port in 1774 only strenghthened and unified colonial resistance. In May of 1775, England sent three more generals (Clinton, Howe, and Burgoyne -- the "Junto") to replace General Gage's command in Massachusetts and to teach the colonies their place, once and for all.

The verses of this song outline England's intentions to make the colonies pay. The lighthearted tune suggests the delight that the generals will take in their task.

'Tis mon-ey makes the mem-ber vote and sanc-ti-fies our ways, It

makes the pa-triot turn his coat, It makes the pa-triot

turn his coat and mon-ey we must raise- and mon-ey we must

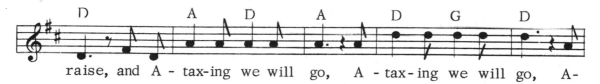

raise, and A-tax-ing we will go, A-tax-ing we will go, A-

tax-ing we-will go - -, A-tax-ing we will go.

'TIS money makes the member vote
And sanctifies our ways
It makes the patriot turn his coat
And money we must raise, and
  A-taxing we will go, &c.
More taxes we must sure impose
To raise the civil list;
Also pay our ayes and noes,
And make opposers hist, and
  A-taxing we will go, &c.
The power supreme of Parliament
Our purpose did assist.
And taxing laws abroad were sent
Which rebels do resist, and
  A-taxing we will go, &c.

Boston we shall in ashes lay,
It is a nest of knaves;
We'll make them soon for mercy pray
Or send them to their graves, and
  A-taxing we will go, &c.
Each colony, we will propose,
Shall raise an ample sum;
Which well applied, under the rose,
May bribe them -- as at home,
  A-taxing we will go, &c.
We'll force and fraud in one unite,
To bring them to our hands;
Then lay a tax on the sun's light
And king's tax on their lands, and
  A-taxing we will go, &c.

29

The *Irishman's* Epistle to the
OFFICERS & TROOPS at *BOSTON*

Tune: THE IRISH WASHERWOMAN

THIS song, first published in May, 1775 in the PENNSYLVANIA MAGAZINE, gloats over the British retreat after the battles of Lexington and Concord. The British forces in Boston had advanced into the neighboring countryside to destroy the rebels' stockpile of arms at Concord. Thanks to Paul Revere's famous ride, their attempt at secrecy failed. At Lexington, militia men engaged the British in a battle in which several colonists were killed. In Concord, some 150 militia men awaited the British at the North Bridge. The British were the first to fire, but the colonists stood their ground and fired back. Under continued harassment, the British force retreated all the way to the Bunker Hill encampment in Charlestown, where they were besieged by colonial militia.

By my faith but I think you're all mak-ers of bulls with your brains in your breech-es your bums in your skulls -, Get home with your mus-kets and put up your swords -, and look in your books for the mean-ing of words. You see, now, my hon-eys, how much you're mis-tak-en, For Con-cord by dis-cord can nev-er be tak-en.

BY my faith but I think ye' re all makers of bulls,
With your brains in your breeches, your bums in your skulls,
Get home with your muskets and put up your swords,
And look in your books for the meaning of words.
You see, now, my honeys, how much you're mistaken,
For Concord by discord can never be taken.

How brave ye went out with your muskets all bright,
And thought to be-frighten the folks with the sight;
But when you got there how they powdered your pums,
And all the way home how they peppered your bums.
And is it not, honeys, a comical crack,
To be proud in the face, and be shot in the back?

How come ye to think, now, they did not know how,
To be after their firelocks as smartly as you?
Why, you see, now, my honeys, 'tis nothing at all,
But to pull at the trigger, and pop goes the ball.

And what have you got now with all your designing,
But a town without victuals to sit down and dine in,
And to look on the ground like a parcel of noodles,
And sing how the Yankees have beaten the Doodles.
I'm sure if you're wise you'll make peace for a dinner,
For fighting and fasting will soon make ye thinner.

The KING'S own REGULARS
And their Triumph over the Irregulars

a new song, to the tune of "An old courtier of the Queen's, and the Queen's old courtier" which is a kind of recitation, like the chanting of the prose psalms in cathedrals.[1]

WHEN the British evacuated Boston in March of 1776, the colonies were triumphant but uneasy. On March 30, this reassuring song about famous British retreats appeared in a Philadelphia newspaper with the following introductory comments:

"The ministry have boasted much of their **regular**, their disciplined troops, which they fancied capable of beating all the **irregulars** in the world. One would wonder how men of any attention to what has passed, could deceive themselves into such an opinion, when so many FACTS within the memory of men not very old evince the contrary.

"The following Yankee song gives us a pretty little collection of those facts, and is printed for the encouragement of our militia; for though it is not safe for men too much to despise their enemies, it is of use that they should have a good opinion of themselves, if just, when compared to those they are to fight with..."[2]

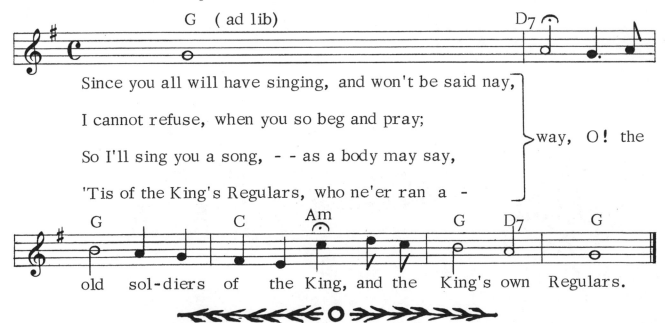

Since you all will have singing, and won't be said nay,

I cannot refuse, when you so beg and pray;

So I'll sing you a song, - - as a body may say,

'Tis of the King's Regulars, who ne'er ran a-

way, O! the old sol-diers of the King, and the King's own Regulars.

SINCE you all will have singing, and won't be said nay,
I cannot refuse, when you so beg and pray;
So I'll sing you a song, -- as a body may say,
'Tis of the King's regulars, who ne'er ran away.
O! the old soldiers of the King, and the King's own Regulars.

No troops perform better than we at reviews,
We march and we wheel and whatever you choose,
George would see how we fight, and we never refuse,
There we all fight with courage -- you may see't in the news.
O! the old soldiers of the King, and the King's own Regulars.

To Monongahela, with fifes and with drums,
We marched in fine order, with cannon and bombs;
That great expedition cost infinite sums,
But a few irregulars cut us all to crumbs.
O! the old soldiers of the King, and the King's own Regulars.

It was not fair to shoot at us from behind trees,
If they had stood open, as they ought, before our great guns, we
            should have beat them with ease,
They may fight with one another that way if they please,
But it is not regular to stand, and fight with such rascals as these.
O! the old soldiers of the King, and the King's own Regulars.

Our general, a council of war did advise
How at Lexington we might the Yankees surprise,
We marched -- and remarched -- all surprise -- at being beat;
And so our wise general's plan of surprise -- was complete.
O! the old soldiers of the King, and the King's own Regulars.

For fifteen miles, they followed and pelted us, we scarce had time to
            pull a trigger;
But did you ever know a retreat performed with more vigor:
For we did it in two hours, which saved us from perdition,
'Twas not in going out, but in returning, consisted our expedition.
O! the old soldiers of the King, and the King's own Regulars.

As they would not get before us, how could they look us in the face?
We took care that they shouldn't, by scampering away apace.
That they had not much to brag of, is a very plain case;
For if they beat us in the fight, we beat them in the race.
O! the old soldiers of the King, and the King's own Regulars.

A NEW War Song
by Sir Peter Parker

Tune: COME, LET US PREPARE

THE unfortunate Sir Peter Parker became the object of many jokes, both in England and America, after his defeat at Sullivan's Island in June of 1776. He commanded the British flagship Bristol and a sizable convoy conducting General Clinton's army to the proposed invasion of Charleston, South Carolina.

The fort on Sullivan's Island, which guarded the entrance to Charleston harbor, was attacked from close range by Sir Peter's ships. While gallantly directing operations through the crossfire, Sir Peter suffered the indignity of having his breeches blown assunder.

The entire action was a disaster for the British, who ultimately re-embarked and sailed for New York. The song, written and printed in London, takes the form of Sir Peter's report on the incident to parliament.

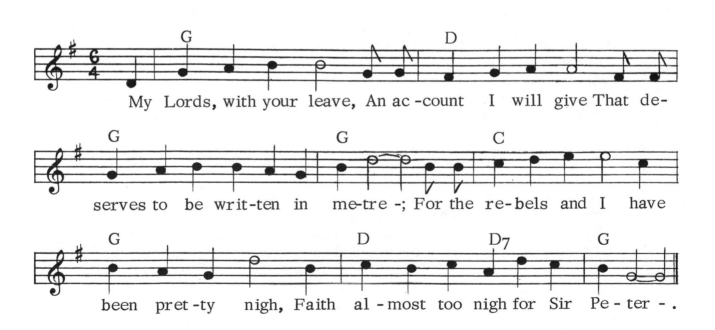

My Lords, with your leave, An ac-count I will give That de-serves to be writ-ten in me-tre -; For the re-bels and I have been pret-ty nigh, Faith al-most too nigh for Sir Pe-ter -.

MY lords with your leave
An account I will give
That deserves to be written in metre
For the rebels and I
Have been pretty nigh
Faith almost too nigh for Sir Peter.

With much labor and toil,
Unto Sullivan's Isle,
I came firm as Falstaff or Pistol,
But the Yankees, 'od rot 'em,
I could not get at 'em,
Most terribly mauled my poor Bristol.

Bold Clinton by land
Did quietly stand
While I made a thundering clatter;
But the channel was deep,
So he could only peep,
And not venture over the water.

De'el take 'em, their shot
Came so swift and so hot
And the cowardly dogs stood so stiff sirs!
That I put ship about
And was glad to get out
Or they would not have left me a skiff sirs!

Now bold as a Turk
I proceed to New York,
Where with Clinton and Howe you may find me.
I've the wind in my tail
And am hoisting my sail,
To leave Sullivan's island behind me.

But my Lords, do not fear,
For before the next year,
Although a small island could fret us,
The Continent whole,
We shall take, by my soul
If the cowardly Yankees will let us.

The CONGRESS

Tune: NANCY DAWSON

After two-hundred years, it is difficult for Americans to imagine how utterly outrageous the behavior, or even the existence, of the Continental Congress must have seemed to the average law-abiding British colonist. Loyalists watched in shocked dismay as the unprecedented collective body challenged England's authority in one act of folly after another, refusing to pay taxes, raising a militia against the king's soldiers, declaring acts of Parliament to be illegal, and, most monstrous of all, declaring the colonies to be independent of the mother country! That the Congress itself should presume to fill the void left by the former monarch was too absurd.

In this song, the loyal poet suggests that it is time to do away with the Congress and restore law and order to the realm.

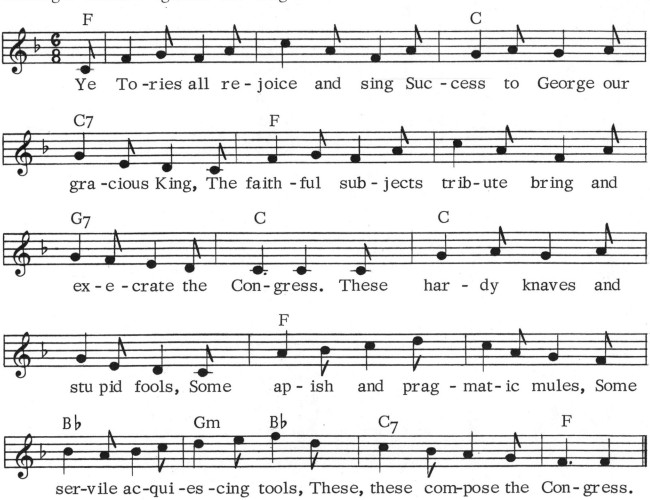

Ye To-ries all re-joice and sing Suc-cess to George our gra-cious King, The faith-ful sub-jects trib-ute bring and ex-e-crate the Con-gress. These har-dy knaves and stu pid fools, Some ap-ish and prag-mat-ic mules, Some ser-vile ac-qui-es-cing tools, These, these com-pose the Con-gress.

YE Tories all rejoice and sing
Success to George our gracious King,
The faithful subjects tribute bring
And execrate the Congress.
These hardy knaves and stupid fools,
Some apish and pragmatic mules,
Some servile acquiescing tools,
These, these compose the Congress.

Then Jove resolved to send a curse,
And all the woes of life rehearse
Not plague, not famine, but much worse
He cursed us with a Congress.
Then peace forsook this hopeless shore
Then cannons blazed with horrid roar
We hear of blood, death, wounds and gore,
The Offspring of the Congress.

With poverty and dire distress
With standing armies us oppress,
Whole troops to Pluto swiftly press;
As victims of the Congress.
Time-serving priests to zealots preach,
Who King and Parliament impeach;
Seditious lessons to us teach
At the command of Congress.

Prepare, prepare, my friends prepare
For scenes of blood, the field of war;
To   royal standard we'll repair,
And curse the haughty Congress.
Huzza! Huzza! and thrice Huzza!
Return peace, harmony and law!
Restore such times as once we saw
And bid adieu to Congress.

A WAR SONG

Tune: PORTSMOUTH

After the Declaration of Independence, all of the participating colonies knew that they must be prepared for the worst. This song expresses the "Spirit of '76", but with a tender touch. It reflects the pain of former British subjects forced to regard their parent state as an enemy and the sorrow of soldiers anticipating separation from their loved ones.

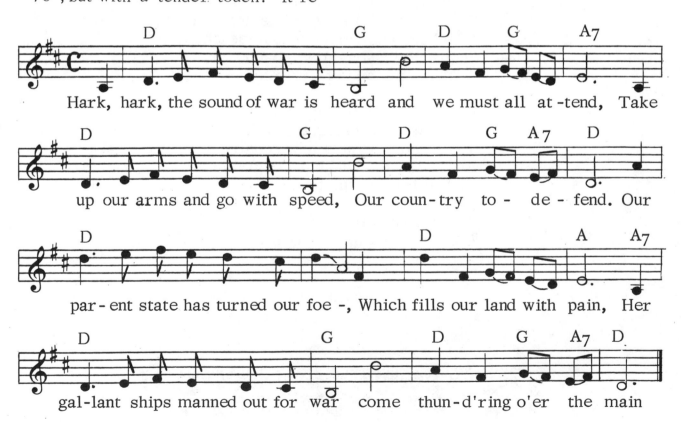

Hark, hark, the sound of war is heard and we must all at-tend, Take up our arms and go with speed, Our coun-try to - de - fend. Our par-ent state has turned our foe -, Which fills our land with pain, Her gal-lant ships manned out for war come thun-d'ring o'er the main

HARK, hark, the sound of war is heard,
And we must all attend
Take up our arms and go with speed,
Our country to defend.
Our parent state has turned our foe,
Which fills our land with pain;
Her gallant ships, manned out for war,
Come thundering o'er the main.

There's Carleton, Howe, and Clinton, too,
And many thousands more,
May cross the sea, but all in vain
Our rights we'll ne' er give o'er.
Our pleasant homes they do invade,
Our property devour;
And all because we won't submit
To their despotic power.

Husbands must leave their loving wives
And sprightly youths attend,
Leave their sweethearts and risk their lives
Their country to defend.
May they be heroes in the field
Have heroes' fame in store;
We pray the Lord to be their shield
Where thundering cannons roar.

Collinet & Phebe

Tune: AS JAMIE GAY

IN this wartime version of a popular Scottish pastoral, the patriotic ideal of virtuous colonial maidenhood is set forth. The joys of courting must be denied until each youth has proven himself worthy by serving his country's cause to final victory.

As Col-lin - et and Phe-be sat Be -neath a pop-lar grove, The

gen-tle youth, with fond -est truth was tell ing - tales of love. "Dear

bloom -ing maid." the shep -herd said, "My ten -der vows - be-

lieve, These down -cast eyes and art -less - sighs, Can

ne'er thy faith de- ceive, Can ne'er - thy faith de - ceive.

AS Collinet and Phebe sat,
Beneath a poplar grove,
The gentle youth, with fondest truth,
Was telling tales of love.
"Dear blooming maid," the shepherd said,
" My tender vows believe,
These downcast eyes, and artless sighs,
Can ne'er thy faith deceive."

"Though some there are, from fair to fair,
Delighting wild to rove,
Such change, thou ne'er from me canst
    fear,
Thy charms secure my love.
Then Phebe now, approve my vow,
By truth, by fondness pressed;
Smile assume to grace thy bloom,
And make thy shepherd bless'd."

A blush o'erspread her cheek with red
Which half she turn'd aside;
With pleasing woes, her bosom rose,
And thus the maid replied --
"Dear gentle youth, I know thy truth,
And all thy arts to please;
But ah! is this a time for bliss,
Or themes as soft as these?"

"While all around, we hear no sound,
But war's terrific strains!
The drum commands our arming bands,
And chides each tardy swain.
Our country's call arouses all,
Who dare to be brave and free!
My love shall crown the youth alone,
Who saves himself and me."

"'Tis done!" he cried, "from thy dear side,
Now quickly I'll be gone;
From love will I, to freedom fly,
A slave to thee alone.
And when I come with laurels home,
And all that freemen crave,
To crown my love, your smiles shall prove
The fair reward the brave."

The Battle of Trenton

Tune: FIRE OF LOVE

THE Battle of Trenton was the first decisive victory of the Continental Army. It occurred during the Christmas season of 1776, when General Washington led his troops on the famous Delaware crossing to surprise an encampment of Hessian mercenaries at Trenton. The victory served to renew rebel hopes. Many pictures, songs, and stories commemorate this event.

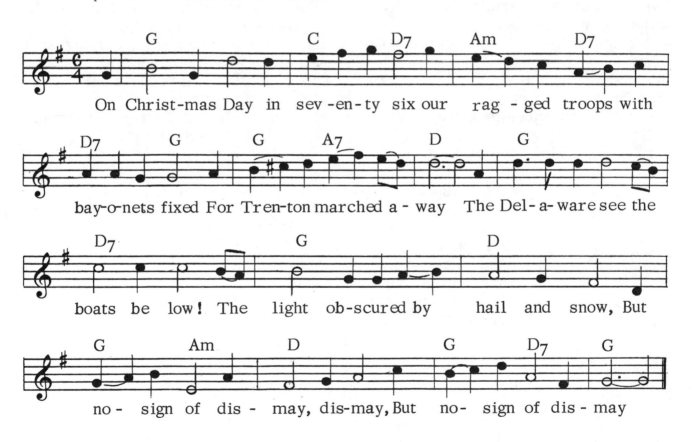

On Christ-mas Day in sev-en-ty six our rag-ged troops with bay-o-nets fixed For Tren-ton marched a-way The Del-a-ware see the boats be low! The light ob-scured by hail and snow, But no-sign of dis-may, dis-may, But no-sign of dis-may

ON Christmas day in '76
Our ragged troops with bayonets fixed
For Trenton marched away.
The Delaware see! The boat below!
The light obscured by hail and snow
But no sign of dismay.

Our object was the Hessian band
That dared invade fair freedom's land,
And quarter in that place.
Great Washington he led us on,
Whose streaming flag in storm or sun,
Had never known disgrace.

In silent march we passed the night,
Each soldier panting for the fight,
Though quite benumbed with frost.
Greene, on the left, at six began,
The fight was led by Sullivan,
Who never a moment lost.

Their pickets stormed, the alarm was spread,
That rebels risen from the dead,
Were marching into town.
Some scampered here, some scampered there,
And some for action did prepare,
But soon their arms laid down.

Now brothers of the patriot bands,
Let's sing deliverance from the hands
Of arbitrary sway.
And as our life is but a span,
Let's touch the tankard while we can,
In memory of that day.

TWO SONGS TO THE TUNE
WAT'RY GOD

WASHINGTON'S victories at Trenton and Princeton inspired a parody on an earlier heroic song. The verses of the original song are shown below; they glorify Lord Hawke, the hero of a British naval battle with the French in 1759. The American parody is on the next page.

THE Wat'ry God great Neptune lay
In Dalliance soft and am'rous play
On Amphitrite's breast.
When uproar reared its horrid head,
The Tritons shrunk, the Neriads fled
And all their fears confest.

Loud Thunder shook the vast Domain,
The Liquid World was wrapt in Flame,
The God Amazed Spoke!
Ye Winds, go forth and make it known
Who dares to shake my Coral Throne,
And fill my Realms with Smoke.

The Winds Obsequious, at his Word
Sprung strongly up t'obey their Lord,
And saw two Fleets aweigh;
One, Victorious Hawke, was Thine,
The other, Conflans' wretched Line,
In terror and dismay.

Appalled, they view Britannia's Sons
Deal Death and Slaughter from their
  guns,
And strike the dreadful Blow!
Which caused ill fated Gallic Slaves
To find a Tomb in briny waves,
And sink to shades below.

With speed they fly, and tell their Chief,
That France was ruined past relief,
And Hawke triumphant rode;
Hawke! cry'd the Fair, pray who is He,
Who dared usurp this power at Sea,
And thus insult a God?

The Winds reply, In distant Lands,
There reigns a King, who Hawke Commands,
He scorns all foreign Force;
And when his floating Castles roll
From Sea to Sea, from Pole to Pole,
Great Hawke directs their Course.

Or when his winged Bullets fly
To punish Fraud and Perfidy,
Or scourge a Guilty Land;
Then gallant Hawke serenely great
Tho' Death and Horror round him wait,
Performs his dread Command.

Neptune with wonder heard the Story,
Of George's sway and Britain's Glory,
Which Time shall ne'er subdue;
Boscawen's Deeds and Saunders' Fame,
Joined with Wolfe's Immortal name,
Then cry'd Can this be true?

A King! He sure must be a God!
Who has such Heroes at his Nod,
To Govern Earth and Sea;
I yield my Trident and my Crown,
A Tribute due to such renown,
Great George shall rule for me.

A PARODY ON
Wat'ry God

IN the new American version, Neptune's legions are replaced by Mars and his retinue, the hero-among-heroes becomes Washington, and Liberty is his commander-in-chief.

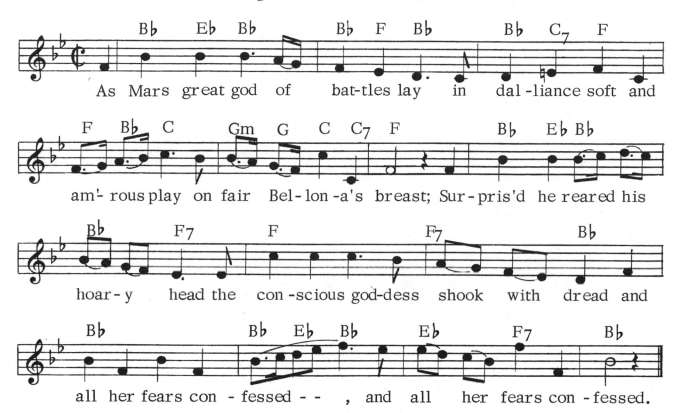

As Mars great god of bat-tles lay in dal-liance soft and am'-rous play on fair Bel-lon-a's breast; Sur-pris'd he reared his hoar-y head the con-scious god-dess shook with dread and all her fears con-fessed - - , and all her fears con-fessed.

AS Mars, great god of battles! lay
   In dalliance soft and amorous play,
On fair Bellona's breast;
Surprised he reared his hoary head,
The conscious goddess shook with dread,
And all her fears confessed.

Loud thunder rolled through Heaven's domain,
The ethereal world was wrapt in flame,
The god amazed spoke:
Go forth, ye powers, and make it known,
Who dares thus boldly shake my throne,
And fill my realms with smoke.

The gods, obsequious to his word,
Sprang swiftly forth t'obey their lord,
And saw two hosts away;
The one, great Washington, was thine;
The other, Howe's disordered line,
In sorrow and dismay.

Appalled they viewed Columbia's sons,
Deal death and slaughter from their guns,
And strike a dreadful blow,
Which made ill-fated British slaves,
On distant shores to find their graves,
And sink to shades below.

Amazed they tell of battles won,
That Britain's ruined; Washington
Alone triumphant rode;
Ha! cries fair, pray who is he
That dares reverse e'en Jove's decree
And thus insult a god?

The gods reply, In yonder lands,
Great Liberty alone commands,
And gives the hero force;
And when his thundering cannon roar,
And strike with dread earth's distant shore,
'Tis she directs their course.

And when her winged bullets fly,
To check a tyrant's treachery,
And lay his glories low;
Then Washington serenely great,
Tho' death and carnage round him wait,
Performs the dreadful blow.

The god with wonder heard the story,
Astonished viewed Columbia's glory,
Which time can ne'er subdue,
Great Warren's deed, and Gates's fame,
Joined to great Lee's immortal name;
And cried, Can this be true?

Britain shall cease to plague mankind,
With sister tyrants strive to bind,
And check the free-born soul;
To Washington her trophies yield,
Freedom shall triumph in the field,
And rule from pole to pole.

A SONG About CHARLESTON

THE British used the same tune to celebrate their conquest of Charleston in 1780. In this version, John Hancock appears as an arrogant usurper of high places, who is dethroned by General Clinton, with the approval of Mars.

KING Hancock sat in regal state,
And big with pride and vainly great,
Addressed his rebel crew,
These haughty Britons soon shall yield
The boasted honors of the field,
While our brave sons pursue.

Six thousand fighting men or more,
Protect the Carolina shore,
And Freedom will defend;
And stubborn Britons soon shall feel,
'Gainst Charleston, and hearts of steel,
How vainly they contend.

But ere he spake in dread array,
To rebel foes, ill-fated day,
The British boys appear;
Their mien with martial ardor fired,
And by their country's wrongs inspired,
Shook Lincoln's heart with fear.

See Clinton brave, serene, and great,
For might deeds revered by fate,
Direct the thundering fight,
While Mars, propitious God of war,
Looks down from his triumphal car,
With wonder and delight.

"Clinton," he cries, "the palm is thine,
Midst heroes thou wert born to shine,
A great immortal name,
And Cornwallis' mighty deeds appear,
Conspicuous each revolving year,
The pledge of future fame."

Our tars, their share of glories won,
For they among the bravest shone,
Undaunted, firm and bold.
Whene'er engaged, their ardor showed
Hearts which with native valor glowed
Hearts of true British mold.

THE FATE OF

JOHN BURGOYNE

Tune: WHITE COCKADE

THE song presented here is one of many written about the defeat of the British general, "John Burgoyne, Esq., Lieutenant-General in his Majesty's armies in America, Colonel of the Queen's regiment of light dragoons, Governor of Fort William in North Britain, one of the representatives of the Commons of Great Britain in Parliament, and commanding an army and fleet employed on an expedition from Canada, etc., etc., ..."[1] Thus did the general describe himself in a haughty proclamation sent before his invading army, stating the terms of surrender demanded of those about to be conquered.

Burgoyne's army moved from Montreal to Fort Ticonderoga and southward toward Albany, where the planned convergence with two other British forces would complete the isolation of troublesome New England. The difficult progress of Burgoyne's men through the untouched forest lands south of Ticonderoga was further hampered by American guerrillas from the surrounding countryside who har-
assed them at every step. When the other British contingents failed to appear, Burgoyne was forced to surrender at Saratoga on October 17, 1777.

A decisive victory of such proportions, involving prisoners of high rank, was a great boost to the Americans. In a proposed exchange of the prisoner-general, alluding to the pompous proclamation quoted above, Governor William Livingston of New Jersey said, "...we can get in exchange for him one Esquire, two Major-Generals, three Colonels of light horse, two Governors, one Member of Congress, the Admiral of our navy, one Commander in Chief in a separate department, and six privates."[2]

St. Clair, mentioned in the last verse, was the American officer in charge of Fort Ticonderoga who retreated before Burgoyne but later rallied his forces and aided in the final victory. Benedict Arnold, still loyal to America at this date, stopped the British contingent moving in from the west; General Gates accepted the final surrender of Burgoyne.

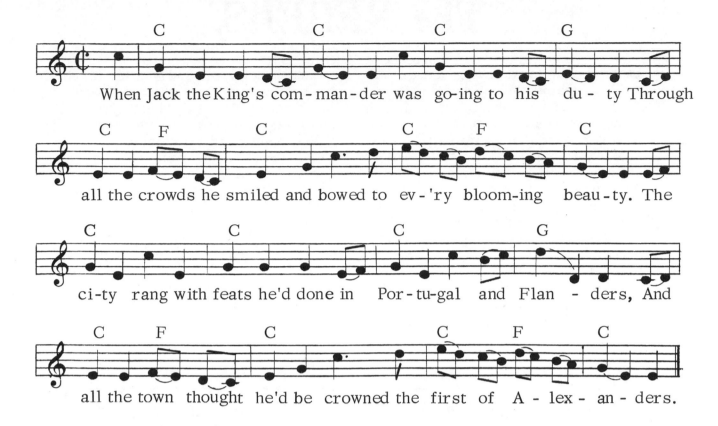

When Jack the King's com-man-der was go-ing to his du-ty Through
all the crowds he smiled and bowed to ev-'ry bloom-ing beau-ty. The
ci-ty rang with feats he'd done in Por-tu-gal and Flan-ders, And
all the town thought he'd be crowned the first of A-lex-an-ders.

WHEN Jack, the King's commander
Was going to his duty
Through all the crowd he smiled and bowed
To every blooming beauty
The city rung with feats he'd done,
In Portugal and Flanders,
And all the town thought he'd be crowned
The first of Alexanders.

To Hampton Court he first repairs,
To kiss great George's hand, sirs,
Then to harangue on state affairs,
Before he left the land, sirs.
The "lower house" sat mute as mouse
To hear his grand oration
And "all the peers" with loudest cheers
Proclaimed him to the nation.

Then off he went to Canada
Next to Ticonderoga
And quitting those, away he goes
Straightway to Saratoga.
With great parade his march he made
To gain his wished for station
When far and wide his minions hied
To spread his "Proclamation".

To such as staid he offers made
Of "pardon on submission
But savage bands should waste the lands
Of all in opposition."
But ah! the cruel fate of war!
This boasted son of Britain
When mounting his triumphal car
With sudden fear was smitten.

The Sons of Freedom gathered round,
His hostile bands confounded
And when they'd fain have turned their back
They found themselves surrounded!
In vain they fought, in vain they fled
Their chief, humane and tender,
To save the rest, soon thought it best
His forces to surrender.

Brave St. Clair when he first retired
Knew what the fates portended
And Arnold and heroic Gates
His conduct have defended.
Thus may America's brave sons
With honor be rewarded,
And be the fate of all her foes
The same as here recorded.

The REBELS

Tune: BLACK JOAK

THIS loyal song lashes out against the rebel colonials and their lawless ways, ridicules their lack of professionalism in governmental and military affairs, and expresses contempt for their clothing and personal habits. From the beginning of the resistance, British factions were scornful of the informal battle procedures of the Continental Army, which always placed expediency before etiquette. As for their clothing, only a small percentage of Continental Army units could afford official uniforms; the rest went to war in their civilian clothes. The chorus of the song refers to those soldiers from the backwoods and frontier territories who fought for their rights wearing fringed buckskin hunting-shirts and carrying their hunting rifles rather than the standard army musket.

However indecorous the appearance of the riflemen, their spiral-bored weapons gave them an enormous advantage in shooting-range over the muskets of the well-dressed enemy, while their years of hunting experience had made them expert marksmen, unaccustomed to wasting their powder. Their contribution to the final victory has been evaluated as substantial, if not decisive.

Ye brave, hon-est sub-jects, who dare to be loy-al, And have stood the brunt of ev-'ry tri-al of hunt-ing shirts and ri-fle guns; Come lis-ten a while and I'll sing you a song, I'll show you those Yan-kees are all in the wrong, Who with blus-t'ring look and most awk-ward gait, 'Gainst their law-ful sov-er-eign dare for to prate with their hunt-ing shirts and ri-fle guns.

YE brave, honest subjects, who dare to be loyal,
And have stood the brunt of every trial,
        Of hunting-shirts and rifle-guns;
Come listen awhile, and I'll tell you a song;
I'll show you those Yankees are all in the wrong,
Who, with blustering look and most awful gait,
'Gainst their lawful sovereign dare for to prate,
        With their hunting-shirts and rifle-guns.

The arch-rebels, barefooted tatterdemalions,
In baseness exceed all other rebellions,
        With their hunting-shirts and rifle-guns:
To rend the empire, the most infamous   lies,
Their mock-patriot Congress, do always devise;
Independence, like the first of rebels, they claim,
But their plots will be damned in the annals of fame,
        With their hunting-shirts and rifle-guns.

Forgetting the mercies of Great Britain's king,
Who saved their forefathers' necks from the string;
        With their hunting-shirts and rifle-guns.
They renounce allegiance and take up their arms,
Assemble together like hornets in swarms,
So dirty their backs, and so wretched their show,
That carrion-crow follows wherever they go,
        With their hunting-shirts and rifle-guns.

With loud peals of laughter, your sides, sirs, would crack,
To see General Convict and Colonel Shoe-Black,
        With their hunting-shirts and rifle-guns.
See cobblers and quacks, rebel priests and the like,
Pettifoggers and barbers, with sword and with pike,
And strutting the standard of Satan beside,
And honest names using, their black deeds to hide,
        With their hunting-shirts and rifle-guns.

For one lawful ruler, many tyrants we've got,
Who force young and old to their wars, to be shot,
     With their hunting-shirts and rifle-guns.
Our good king, God speed him! never used men so,
We then could speak, act, and like freemen could go;
But committees enslave us, our Liberty's gone,
Our trade and church murdered; our country's undone.
     By hunting-shirts and rifle-guns.

Come take up your glasses, each true loyal heart,
And may every rebel meet his due desert,
     With his hunting-shirt and rifle-gun.
May Congress, Conventions, those damned inquisitions,
Be fed with hot sulphur, from Lucifer's kitchens,
May commerce and peace again be restored,
And Americans own their true sovereign lord.
     Then oblivion to shirts and rifle-guns.
      God save the King.

The British Light Infantry

Tune: BLACK SLOVEN

A loyalist newspaper in New York carried this spirited song describing the exemplary qualities of one British army unit that fought in the Revolution. According to Moore, another song about the same unit was current in America, but was unfit to print.

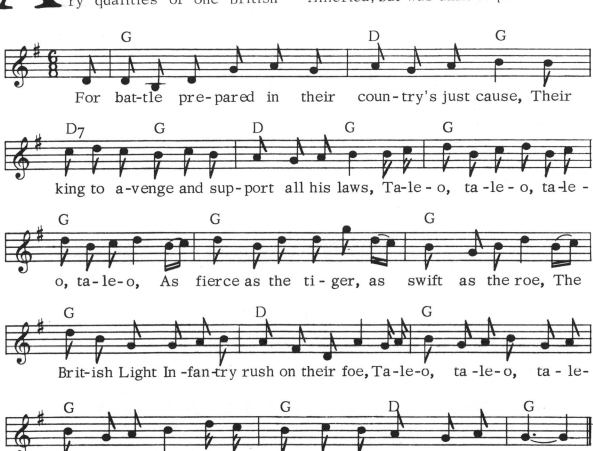

For bat-tle pre-pared in their coun-try's just cause, Their king to a-venge and sup-port all his laws, Ta-le - o, ta-le - o, ta-le - o, ta-le-o, As fierce as the ti - ger, as swift as the roe, The Brit-ish Light In-fan-try rush on their foe, Ta-le-o, ta-le-o, ta-le - o, ta-le - o, Ta-le - o, ta-le - o, ta-le - o - -.

FOR battle prepared in their country's just cause,
Their king to avenge and support all his laws;
As fierce as a tiger, as swift as the roe,
The British Light Infantry rush on their foe. Taleo, &c.

Though rebels unnumbered oppose their career,
Their hearts are undaunted; they're strangers to fear;
No obstacles hinder; resistless they go,
And death and destruction attend every blow. Taleo, &c.

The alarm of the drum and the cannon's loud roar;
The musket's quick flash, but inflames them the more.
No dangers appal, for they fear no control,
But glory and conquest inspires every soul. Taleo, &c.

Whenever their foe stands arranged in their sight,
With ardor impatient they pant for the fight;
Rout, havoc, confusion they spread through the field,
And rebellion and treason are forced to yield. Taleo, &c.

53

The HALCYON Days of Old *ENGLAND*

Or the Wisdom of Administration Demonstrated

Tune: YE MEDLEY OF MORTALS

EARLY in 1778, the people of England began to feel the effects of the American conflict in ways that could not be ignored. After Burgoyne's surprising defeat, many officers from upper-class English families found themselves prisoners of war. Losses of British troops were mounting, while apathy of the people toward a war so remote forced the government to hire soldiers from Scotland, Ireland, and Germany. Instead of providing peacetime tax relief for Britons, the American colonies were exacting new and heavy war taxes from them.

As involvement grew and the British treasury diminished, Lord North led a parliamentary move toward an early end to the conflict through modification of England's rigid stance. After a bitter fight, the Parliament passed the Conciliatory Propositions, which met nearly all the previous demands of the colonies.

This song, published in a London newspaper in 1778, expressed popular attitudes which may have influenced some members of Parliament to vote for the Conciliatory Acts. The song retained its popularity among Americans long after the Conciliatory Acts had been unanimously rejected by Congress.

Give ear to my song, I'll not tell you a sto-ry; This is the bright e-ra of Old Eng-land's glo-ry! And though some may think us in pi-ti-ful plight, I'll swear they're mis-ta-ken for mat-ters go right! Sing tan-ta-ra-ra-ra, Wise all! Wise all! Sing tan-ta-ra-ra-ra, Wise all - !

GIVE ear to my song, I'll not tell you a story
This is the bright era of Old England's glory!
And though some may think us in pitiful plight
I'll swear they're mistaken, for matters go right!
      Sing tantararara, Wise all! Wise all!
      Sing tantararara, Wise all.
Let us laugh at the cavils of weak silly elves!
Our statesmen are wise men! they say so themselves,
And tho' little mortals may hear it with wonder,
'Tis consummate wisdom that causes each blunder!
      Sing tantararara, &c.
They are now engaged in a glorious war!
It began about tea, about feathers and tar;
With spirit they push what they've planned with sense!
Forty millions they've spent for a tax of three pence.
      Sing tantararara, &c.
The debts of the nation do grieve them so sore,
To lighten our burden, they load us the more!
They aim at th' American cash, my dear honey!
Yet beggar this kingdom, and send them the money.
      Sing tantararara, &c.
What honors we're gaining by taking their forts,
Destroying bateaus, and blocking up ports!
Burgoyne would have worked 'em but for a mishap,
By Gates and one Arnold, he's caught in a trap!
      Sing tantararara, &c.
Oh! think us not cruel, because our allies
Are savagely scalping men, women and boys!
Maternal affection to this step doth move us!
The more they are scalped, the more they will love us.
      Sing tantararara, &c.
Some folks are uneasy, and make a great pother
For the loss of one army, and half of another;
But, sirs, next campaign by ten thousands we'll slay 'em,
If we can find soldiers, and money to pay 'em.
      Sing tantararara, &c.
I've sung you a song, now I'll give you a prayer;
May peace soon succeed to this horrible war!
Again may we live with our brethren in concord,
And the authors of mischief all hang on a strong cord.
      Sing tantararara, &c.

THE YANKEES

RETURN FROM CAMP.

FATHER and I went down to camp,
Along with captain Gooding,
There we see the men and boys,
As thick as hasty pudding.
Yankey doodle, keep it up,
Yankey doodle, dandy ;
CHORUS. *Mind the music and the step,*
And with the girls be handy.

And there we see a thousand men,
As rich as 'Squire David ;
And what they wasted every day,
I wish it could be saved.
Yankey doodle, &c.

The 'lasses they eat every day,
Would keep an house a winter ;
They have as much that I'll be bound
They eat it when they're amind to.
Yankey doodle, &c.

And there we see a swamping gun,
Large as a log of maple,
Upon a deuced little cart,
A load for father's cattle.
Yankey doodle, &c.

And every time they shoot it off,
It takes a horn of powder ;
It makes a noise like father's gun,
Only a nation louder.
Yankey doodle, &c.

I went as nigh to one myself,
As 'Siah's underpining ;
And father went as nigh again,
I thought the deuce was in him.
Yankey doodle, &c.

Cousin Simon grew so bold,
I thought he would have cock'd it :
It scar'd me so, I shrink'd it off,
And hung by father's pocket.
Yankey doodle, &c.

And Captain Davis had a gun,
He kind of clap'd his hand on't,

And struck a crooked stabbing iron
Upon the little end on't.
Yankey doodle, &c.

And there I see a pumpkin shell
As big as mother's bason,
And every time they touch'd it off,
They scamper'd like the nation.
Yankey doodle, &c.

I see a little barrel too,
The heads were made of leather,
They knock'd upon't with little clubs,
And call'd the folks together.
Yankey doodle, &c.

And there was Captain Washington,
And gentlefolks about him,
They say he's grown so tarnal proud,
He will not ride without 'em.
Yankey doodle, &c.

He got him on his meeting clothes,
Upon a slapping stallion,
He set the world along in rows,
In hundred and in millions.
Yankey doodle, &c.

The flaming ribbons in their hats,
They look'd so taring fine, ah,
I wanted pockily to get,
To give to my Jemimah.
Yankey doodle, &c.

I see another snarl of men
A digging graves, they told me,
So tarnal long, so tarnal deep,
They 'tended they should hold me.
Yankee doodle, &c.

It scar'd me so, I hook'd it off,
Nor stopt, as I remember,
Nor turn'd about till I got home,
Lock'd up in mother's chamber.
Yankey doodle, &c.

N. COVERLY, jr. Printer, *Milk-Street, Boston.*

THE YANKEES RETURN FROM CAMP. Broadside; Boston, between 1805 and 1814. Courtesy, The American Antiquarian Society.

THREE SONGS

TO THE TUNE

YANKEE DOODLE

VERSES written to the tune of YANKEE DOODLE in an American ballad-opera of 1767 indicate that the song was already well-known in the colonies before the Revolution. It was certainly one of the most popular settings for new ballads by both factions after hostilities began. Perhaps the best-known versions are those which emphasize the naivete and unpolished manners of the rural colonists. (See broadside on page opposite.)

The adoption of YANKEE DOODLE as a British army marching tune during maneuvers against the colonists carried derogatory implications, which the fifers and drummers of the Continental Army turned to good advantage by playing the same tune at British surrender ceremonies. Thus, YANKEE DOODLE evolved during the war from a British tool of ridicule to a symbol of pride and dignity for Americans. Today it is the best-known tune of the Revolutionary period and has acquired a special national status.

There are many unresolved questions connected with the song, including the source of the melody, the original version of the words, and the derivation of the word "Yankee". The interested reader is referred to Oscar Sonneck's definitive work on the subject. [1]

Of the many songs set to YANKEE DOODLE during the Revolution, we have selected three, depicting various phases of the conflict. Their common denominator is derision.

The Battle of the Kegs

THE BATTLE OF THE KEGS relates an event which occurred in 1778 during the British occupation of Philadelphia. A group of rebel colonists charged a quantity of kegs with powder, so that they would explode upon contact. The innocent-looking devices, later called "infernals" by the British, were floated down the Delaware River past the fleet of enemy ships at anchor there. When British sailors observed the kegs passing by, officers gave the order to fire, and soon the sound of exploding kegs drew all the British soldiers from the city to repel the attack. The incident consumed a large quantity of British ammunition, while the frantic activity of the British forces provided an amusing spectacle for Philadelphians, who gathered at the wharves to watch.

The author of the verses was the poet-composer, Francis Hopkinson, who may have been an eyewitness to the battle.

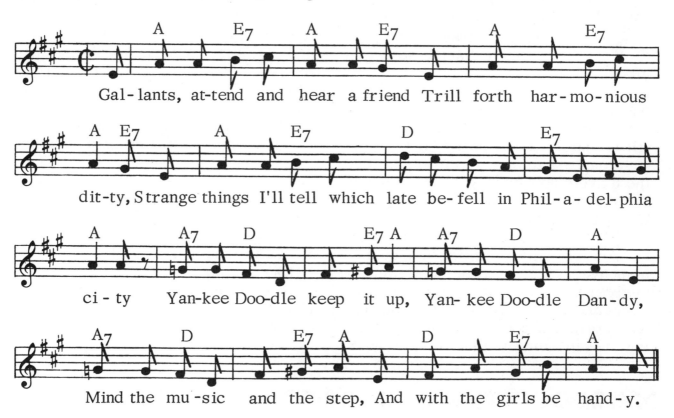

Gal-lants, at-tend and hear a friend Trill forth har-mo-nious dit-ty, Strange things I'll tell which late be-fell in Phil-a-del-phia ci-ty Yan-kee Doo-dle keep it up, Yan-kee Doo-dle Dan-dy, Mind the mu-sic and the step, And with the girls be hand-y.

GALLANTS attend and hear a friend
  Trill forth harmonious ditty,
Strange things I'll tell, which late befell
In Philadelphia city.
    Yankee Doodle keep it up,
    Yankee Doodle Dandy,
    Mind the music and the step,
    And with the girls be handy.
'Twas early day, as poets say,
Just when the sun was rising,
A soldier stood, on log of wood,
And saw a thing surprising.
    Yankee Doodle, etc.
As in amaze he stood to gaze,
The truth can't be denied, sir,
He spied a score of kegs or more
Come floating down the tide, sir.
    Yankee Doodle, etc.
A sailor, too, in jerkin blue,
This strange appearance viewing,
First damn'd his eyes, in great surprise,
Then said, "Some mischief's brewing".
    Yankee Doodle, etc.
"These kegs, I'm told, the rebels hold,
Packed up like pickled herring
And they're come down t'attack the town,
In this new way of ferrying.
    Yankee Doodle, etc.
Now up and down, throughout the town
Most frantic scenes were acted;
And some ran here and others there
Like men almost distracted.
    Yankee Doodle, etc.

"Arise, arise!" Sir Erskine cries,
"The rebels -- more's the pity --
Without a boat, are all afloat,
And ranged before the city.
    Yankee Doodle, etc.
Therefore prepare for bloody war;
These kegs must all be routed,
Or surely we despised shall be
And British courage doubted."
    Yankee Doodle, etc.
The royal band, now ready stand
All ranged in dread array, sir,
With stomachs stout, to see it out,
And make a bloody day, sir.
    Yankee Doodle, etc.
The cannons roar from shore to shore.
The small arms make a rattle;
Since wars began, I'm sure no man
E're saw so strange a battle.
    Yankee Doodle, etc.
The kegs,' tis said, though strongly made
Of rebel staves and hoops, sir,
Could not oppose their powerful foes,
The conquering British troops, sir.
    Yankee Doodle, etc.
From morn til night, these men of might
Displayed amazing courage;
And when the sun was fairly down,
Retired to sup their porridge.
    Yankee Doodle, etc.
Such feats did they perform that day,
Against those wicked kegs, sir,
That years to come, if they get home,
They'll make their boasts and brags, sir.
    Yankee Doodle, etc.

YANKEE DOODLE'S
Expedition to
RHODE ISLAND

IN 1778, the Continental Congress received diplomatic recognition from no less a ruler than Louis XVI of France, who pledged equipment and troops to the Americans' cause. Alliance of the rebels with England's most powerful enemy struck fear and apprehension in the hearts of the Loyalists.

One of the first joint efforts undertaken by the new allies was an expedition to Rhode Island. American land troops and a fleet of French ships were to surround British-held Newport and force a surrender. The attack failed, primarily because the French fleet withdrew at an inconvenient moment. Americans were dismayed by the undependability of their new allies, while Loyalists gleefully crowed "We told you so" in songs such as this one.

In the first verse, "Lewis" refers to King Louis XVI of France. M. Gerard was the French envoy who delivered the documents of alliance to the Congress. "Jonathan" of verses 2 and 9 refers to General Sullivan who commanded the American troops. A section of the Massachusetts militia, led by John Hancock, participated in the maneuver, as mentioned in verse 5. Sir Robert Pigot of verse 8 was commander of the British troops in Rhode Island.

FROM Lewis, Monsieur Gerard came,
  To Congress in this town, sir,
They bow'd to him, and he to them,
And then they all sat down, sir.
   Yankee Doodle, etc.
Begar, said Monsier, one grand coup,
You shall bientot behold, sir;
This was believ'd as gospel true,
And Jonathan felt bold, sir.
   Yankee Doodle, etc.
So Yankee Doodle did forget
The sound of British drum, sir,
How oft it made him quake and sweat,
In spite of Yankee rum, sir.
   Yankee Doodle, etc.

He took his wallet on his back,
His rifle on his shoulder,
And vow'd Rhode Island to attack,
Before he was much older.
   Yankee Doodle, etc.
In dread array their tatter'd crew,
Advanc'd with colors spread, sir,
Their fifes played Yankee doodle, doo,
King Hancock at their head, sir.
   Yankee Doodle, etc.
What numbers bravely crossed the seas,
I cannot well determine,
A swarm of rebels and of fleas,
And every other vermin.
   Yankee Doodle, etc.

Their mighty hearts might shrink they tho't
For all flesh only grass is,
A plenteous store they therefore brought,
Of whiskey and molasses.
   Yankee Doodle, etc.
They swore they'd make bold Pigot squeak,
So did their good ally, sir,
And take him pris'ner in a week,
But that was all my eye, sir.
   Yankee Doodle, etc.
As Jonathan so much desir'd
To shine in martial story,
D'Estaing with politesse retir'd,
To leave him all the glory.
   Yankee Doodle, etc.

He left him what was better yet,
At least it was more use, sir,
He left him for a quick retreat,
A very good excuse, sir.
   Yankee Doodle, etc.
To stay, unless he rul'd the sea,
He thought would not be right, sir,
And Continental troops, said he,
On islands should not fight, sir.
   Yankee Doodle, etc.
Another cause with these combin'd
To throw him in the dumps, sir,
For Clinton's name alarmed his mind,
And made him stir his stumps, sir.
   Yankee Doodle, etc.

The RECESS

GREAT Britain's conduct of the war against her American colonies was not without its critics back home. A recess of the Parliament prompted the anonymous author of this song to chide the legislative body for its inef-

fectiveness in the face of a steadily worsening situation. The verses were first published in London, and then appeared on a colonial ballad-sheet in 1779.

AND now our Senators are gone
To take their leave of London
To mourn how little they have done,
How much they have left undone!
   Yankee Doodle, etc.
Heaven bless 'em in their summer
seats,
And grant their neighbors stare at
The long recounting of their feats,
Though wondering much what
they're at!
   Yankee Doodle, etc.
Bless'd be the times when men may
do,
What no one comprehendeth;
May boast of deeds that all must rue,
Nor judge where nonsense endeth!
   Yankee Doodle, etc.
One year, with half ten thousand men,
We swallow all our foes up;
The next, the times are turn'd, and
then
Old England's scale light goes up,
   Yankee Doodle, etc.

But still with courage and with glee,
New laws we must be framing;
With paper and with parchment, we
The savages are taming.
   Yankee Doodle, etc.
We swear the transatlantic folks
Shall all obey our orders;
While they turn all we do to jokes,
And cry out, "guard your borders."
   Yankee Doodle, etc.
Well, then, we'll go to war with France--
Yes -- no -- we must -- we mustn't
John Bull shall teach Monsieur to dance--
But can't -- and there's the curse on't.
   Yankee Doodle, etc.
What's to be done? -- we'll end the jar--
But how? -- Ah! there's the devil --
'Tis easier to provoke a war
By far, than cure the evil.
   Yankee Doodle, etc.
We trust you'll nearer hit the point
When you shall meet next winter;
And if you cannot set the joint,
Be sure reduce the splinter.
   Yankee Doodle, etc.

THE AMERICAN Vicar of Bray

Tune: VICAR OF BRAY

IN times of political unrest, there are always those who manage to avoid commitment. They roll with the blows of changing times, and cooperate with whichever faction is on top to the extent required to ensure survival. The proverbial Vicar of Bray has been associated with a period in English history when the state religion changed with each succeeding monarch, although no historical model has ever been satisfactorily identified. [1]

This song alludes to those colonists with Tory inclinations who avoided a tarring and feathering by rebel zealots and ultimately kept their homes and property, by allowing expediency rather than loyalty to guide their allegiance during the days of conflict. [2] The verses also provide a useful recounting of the main events of the war.

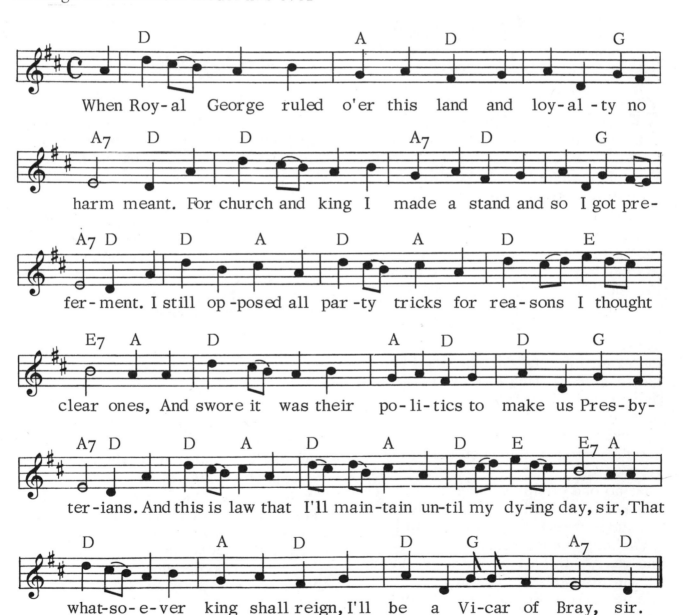

When Roy-al George ruled o'er this land and loy-al-ty no harm meant. For church and king I made a stand and so I got pre-fer-ment. I still op-posed all par-ty tricks for rea-sons I thought clear ones, And swore it was their po-li-tics to make us Pres-by-ter-ians. And this is law that I'll main-tain un-til my dy-ing day, sir, That what-so-e-ver king shall reign, I'll be a Vi-car of Bray, sir.

WHEN Royal George ruled o'er
   this land
And loyalty no harm meant
For church and King I made a stand
And so I got preferment.
I still opposed all party tricks
For reasons I thought clear ones
And swore it was their politics
To make us Presbyterians.
   And this is law that I'll maintain
   Until my dying day, sir,
   Let whatsoever King will reign
   I'll be a Vicar of Bray, sir.
When Stamp Act passed the Parliament
To bring some grist to mill, sir,
To back it was my firm intent
But soon there came repeal, sir.
I quickly joined the common cry
That we should all be slaves, sir
The House of Commons was a sty
The Kings and Lords were knaves, sir.
   And this is law, &c.
Now all went smooth, as smooth could be
I strutted and looked big, sir
And when they laid a tax on tea,
I was believed a Whig, sir;
I laughed at all the vain pretence
Of taxing at a distance,
And swore before I'd pay a pence,
I'd make a firm resistance.
   And this is law, &c.
A Congress now was quickly called
That we might act together.
I thought that Britain would, appalled
Be glad to make fair weather,
And soon repeal the obnoxious bill
As she had done before, sir
That we might gather wealth at will
And so be taxed no more sir.
   And this is law, &c.
But Britain was not quickly seared;
She told another story.
When independence was declared
I figured as a Tory,
Declared it was rebellion base
To take up arms -- I cursed it,
For, faith, it seemed a settled case
That we should soon be worsted.
   And this is law, &c.

The French alliance now came forth;
The Papists flocked in shoals, sir
Friseurs, marquis, valets of birth,
And priests to save our souls, sir
Our "good ally" with towering wing,
Embraced the flattering hope, sir
That we should own him for our King
And then invite the Pope, sir.
   And this is law, &c.
Then Howe with drum and great parade
Marched through this famous town, sir,
I cried, "May fame his temples shade
With laurels for a crown, sir."
With zeal I swore to make amends
To good old Constitution:
And drank confusion to the friends
Of our late Revolution.
   And this is law, &c.
But poor Burgoyne's announced my fate:
The Whigs began to glory.
I now bewailed my wretched state
That e'er I was a Tory.
By night the British left the shore
Nor cared for friends a fig, sir;
I turned the cat in pan once more,
And so became a Whig, sir.
   And this is law, &c.
I called the army butchering dogs,
A bloody tyrant King, sir
The Commons, Lords, a set of rogues
That all deserved to swing, sir.
Since fate has made us great and free,
And Providence can't falter,
So Congress e'er my king shall be...
Unless the times shall alter.
   And this is law, &c.

AN APPEAL TO LOYALISTS

Tune: THE CUTPURSE

AS the war dragged on, and opposition in England became more vocal, the British pursued a plan to conquer America with Americans. Every means was used to strengthen Loyalist opposition to the rebellion and to enlist colonial Tories as soldiers.

The potent language of the following verses played on Loyalist fears and prejudices. Particular emphasis was given to the dire prediction that defeat at the hands of the rebels, now allied with the French, would inevitably lead to state Catholicism and Papal rule.

Wat Tyler and Jack Straw were ringleaders in the English Peasant Revolt of 1381. They led the mobs to acts of violence and murder, and were themselves murdered, in their attempt to defy the king's ministers and change the structure of English society.

The old Eng-lish cause knocks at ev-'ry man's door, And
It ad-dress-es the rich - - as well as the poor, And fair

bids him stand up for re-li-gion and right;
lib-er-ty bids them like Eng-lish-men fight. And suf-fer no

wrong, From a re-bel throng Who, if they're not quelled will en-

slave us ere long; Most brave-ly then let us our lib-er-ty
Or each re-bel cut-purse will soon give us

prize, Nor suf-fer the Con-gress to blind all our eyes;
law, For they are as bad as a Ty-ler or Straw.

THE old English cause knocks at every man's door,
   And bids him stand up for religion and right;
It addresses the rich as well as the poor;
And fair liberty, bids them, like Englishmen fight.
         And suffer no wrong,
         From a rebel throng,
Who, if they're not quelled, will enslave us ere long;
Most bravely then let us our liberty prize,
Nor suffer the Congress to blind all our eyes;
         Or each rebel cut-purse, will soon give us law,
         For they are as bad as a Tyler or Straw.

From France D'Estaing to America has come.
The French banditti will rob our estates;
These robbers are all protected by Rome;
Consult but their annals, record but their dates,
         It's their politics
         To burn heretics,
Or poison by water that's fetched from the Styx.
Let Frenchified rebels, in vain then attempt
To bring our own church, or our king to contempt;
         For no rebel cut-purse shall e'er give us law,
         Should they prove as daring as Tyler or Straw.

The farces of Rome, with carrying her hosts,
Are laugh'd at and jeer'd by the learned and wise,
And all her thin tinsels apparently lost,
Her stories of relics, and sanctified lies.
         Each ignorant joke
         Believe, or you smoke,
And if we are conquered we receive the Pope's yoke;
But despising the counsels of Adams and Lee,
As loyal Americans, we'll die or be free.
         For no rebel cut-throat shall e'er give us law,
         Should they prove as daring as Tyler or Straw.

Let curses most vile, and anathemas roar,
Let half-ruined France, to the Pope tribute pay;
Britain's thundering canon, shall guard safe our shore;
Great George shall defend us, none else we'll obey.
         Then France, join'd by Spain,
         May labor in vain,
For soon the Havana shall be ours again.
The French then will scamper and quit every state,
And find themselves bubbled, when morbleu it's too late.
         For no Frenchman, or rebel imp of the law
         In our old constitution can point out a flaw.

65

CORNWALLIS BURGOYNED

Tune: MAGGIE LAUDER

THE use of "Burgoyne" as a verb in the title of this song indicates to what extent that name had become synonymous with defeat and humiliation. The surrender of General Cornwallis on October 17, 1781 was a cause of particular rejoicing for Americans because of the bru-

tal plunder and destruction committed by his army. Along with Cornwallis' army, Britain lost the will to continue the war. The event signalled the end of official hostilities, although the last British troops did not leave American soil until December of 1783.

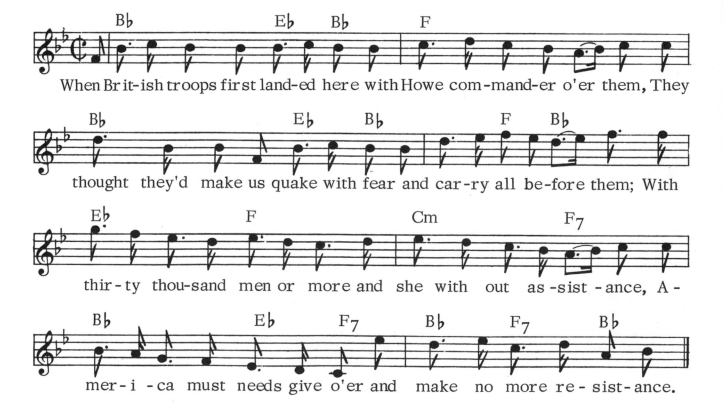

When Brit-ish troops first land-ed here with Howe com-mand-er o'er them, They thought they'd make us quake with fear and car-ry all be-fore them; With thir-ty thou-sand men or more and she with out as-sist-ance, A-mer-i-ca must needs give o'er and make no more re-sist-ance.

WHEN British troops first landed here
With Howe commander o'er them
They thought they'd make us quake for fear
And carry all before them;
With thirty thousand men or more
And she without assistance
America must needs give o'er
And make no more resistance.

But Washington, her glorious son,
Of British hosts the terror
Soon, by repeated overthrows
Convinced them of their error.
Let Princeton and let Trenton tell
What gallant deeds he's done, sir
And Monmouth's plains where hundreds fell
And thousands more have run, sir.

Cornwallis, too, when he approached
Virginia's old dominion
Thought he would soon her conqueror be;
And so was North's opinion
From state to state with rapid stride
His troops had marched before, sir,
Til quite elate with martial pride,
He thought all dangers o'er, sir.

But our allies, to his surprise,
The Chesapeake had entered;
And now too late, he cursed his fate
And wished he ne'er had ventured.
For Washington no sooner knew
The visit he had paid her
Than to his parent state he flew
To crush the bold invader.

When he sat down before the town
His lordship soon surrendered;
His martial pride he laid aside
And cased the British standard.
Gods! How this stroke will North provoke
And all his thoughts confuse, sir!
And how the Peers will hang their ears
When first they hear the news, sir.

Be peace, the glorious end of war,
By this event effected;
And be the name of Washington
To latest times respected.
Then let us toast America
And France in union with her
And may Great Britain rue the day
Her hostile bands came hither.

Hymns

CHESTER

BOTH the words and music of CHESTER were written by William Billings, one of America's earliest composers of church music. A Bostonian by birth and a close friend of Samuel Adams, Billings was a fervent patriot and an ardent supporter of the rebel cause. His quiet, unaggressive nature made him unfit for the extremist activities of the Sons of Liberty, and a physical deformity prevented him from enlisting in the army. He made his contribution to the war effort in the only way possible -- through his music.

The melody of CHESTER became a stirring battle cry to the Continental Army, particularly to those units from New England. Played on fifes and drums and used as a march, it became one of the most popular of all Revolutionary War tunes. It was published in several editions of Billings' hymns during the war years.

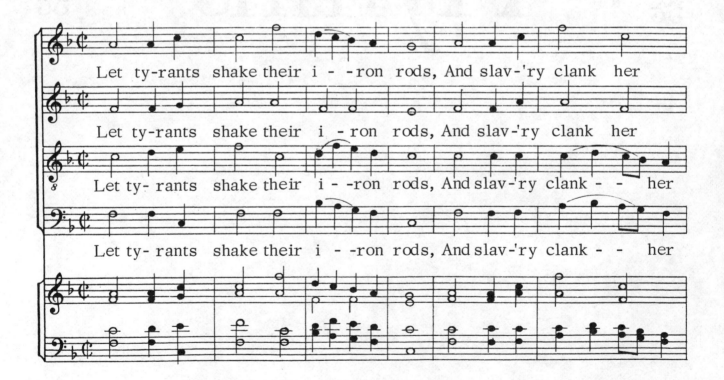

Let ty-rants shake their i--ron rods, And slav-'ry clank her

Let ty-rants shake their i-ron rods, And slav-'ry clank her

Let ty-rants shake their i--ron rods, And slav-'ry clank-- her

Let ty-rants shake their i--ron rods, And slav-'ry clank-- her

LET tyrants shake their iron rods,
And slavery clank her galling chains;
We fear them not; we trust in God --
New England's God forever reigns.

Howe and Burgoyne and Clinton, too,
With Prescott and Cornwallis joined
Together plot our overthrow,
In one infernal league combined.

When God inspired us for the fight,
Their ranks were broke, their lines were forced;
Their ships were shattered in our sight,
Or swiftly driven from our coast.

The foe comes on with haughty stride;
Our troops advance with martial noise;
Their veterans flee before our youth,
And generals yield to beardless boys.

What grateful offering shall we bring?
What shall we render to the Lord?
Loud hallelujahs let us sing,
And praise his name on every chord.

71

BUNKER HILL

THE words of this hymn were taken from "The American Hero, a Sapphic Ode", written by Nathaniel Niles in 1775, and set to music by Andrew Law, a church musician and publisher of many anthologies of hymns. Law named the hymn for the scene of a famous battle near Boston. The verses express the fatalistic point of view that God has determined the hour of death for each of us. Some of the lines call to mind passages from the 23rd Psalm.

Why should vain mor-tals trem-ble at the sight of death and des-truc-tion on the field of bat-tle, Where blood and car-nage, Where blood and

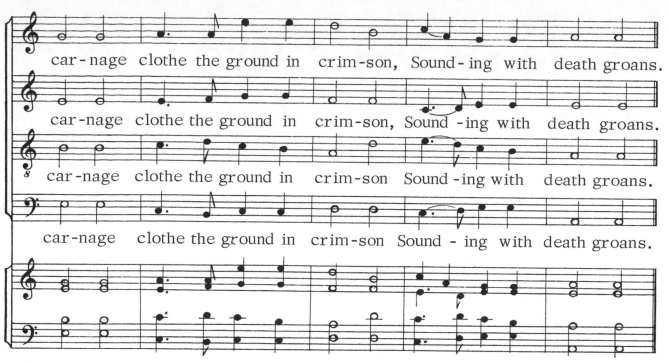

car-nage clothe the ground in crim-son, Sound-ing with death groans.

car-nage clothe the ground in crim-son, Sound-ing with death groans.

car-nage clothe the ground in crim-son Sound-ing with death groans.

car-nage clothe the ground in crim-son Sound-ing with death groans.

WHY should vain mortals tremble at the sight of
Death and destruction on the field of battle,
Where blood and carnage clothe the ground in crimson,
    Sounding with death groans?
Death will invade us by the means appointed,
And we must all bow to the King of Terrors;
Nor am I anxious, if I am prepared,
    What shape he comes in.
Infinite goodness teaches us submission,
Bids us be quiet under all His dealings,
Never repining, but forever praising
    God, our creator.
Good is Jehovah in bestowing sunshine,
Nor less His goodness in the storm and thunder,
Mercies and judgements both proceed from kindness --
    Infinite kindness.
Then to the wisdom of my Lord and Master
I will commit all that I have or wish for.
Sweetly as babes sleep will I give my life up
    When called to yield it.
Let oceans waft on all your floating castles,
Fraught with destruction, horrible to nature;
Then, with your sails filled by a storm of vengeance,
    Bear down to battle!
Fame and dear freedom lure me on to battle,
While a fell despot, grimmer than a death's head,
Stings me with serpents, fiercer than Medusa's
    To the encounter.
Life, for my country and the cause of freedom,
Is but a trifle for a worm to part with; --
And if preserved in so great a contest,
    Life is redoubled.

73

AN ODE FOR THE FOURTH of JULY

INDEPENDENCE Day celebrations were frequently graced with creative efforts by the people. The use of the British national anthem, GOD SAVE THE KING (in the tenor part), does not seem incongruous as a setting for these optimistic American verses.

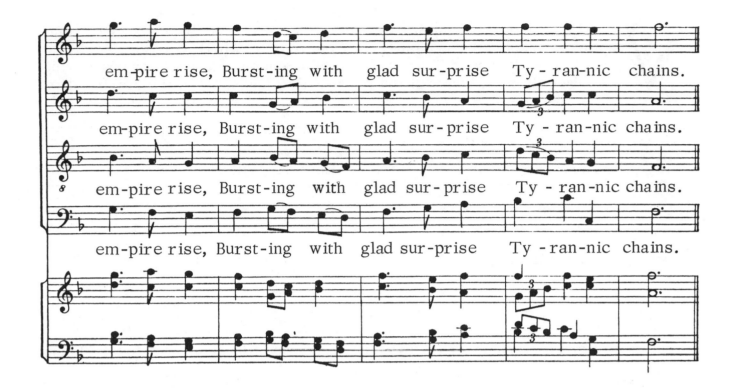

em-pire rise, Burst-ing with glad sur-prise Ty - ran-nic chains.

COME all ye sons of song
Pour the full sound along
In joyful strains
Beneath these Western skies
See a new empire rise,
Bursting with glad surprise
Tyrannic chains.

Liberty with keen eye
Pierced the blue-vaulted sky,
Resolved us free;
From her Imperial seat
Beheld the bleeding state,
Approved this day's debate
And firm decree.

Sublime in awful form,
Above the whirling storm,
The Goddess stood;
She saw with pitying eye,
War's tempest raging high,
Our heroes bravely die,
In fields of blood.

High on his shining car,
Mars, the stern God of war,
Our struggles blest:
Soon victory waved her hand,
Fair Freedom cheered the land,
Led on Columbia's band
To glorious rest.

Now all ye sons of song,
Pour the full sound along,
Who shall control;
For in this western clime,
Freedom shall rise sublime,
Till ever changing time,
Shall cease to roll.

THANKSGIVING HYMN

VERSES for this hymn were composed upon the occasion of a national Day of Thanksgiving declared in honor of the peace-treaty between England and America, ratified by the Continental Congress in April of 1783. The hymn set the tone for the postwar outpouring of patriotic songs and the glorification of General Washington.

The Lord a-bove, in ten - der love, Hath sav'd us from our foes;

The Lord a-bove, in ten - der love, Hath sav'd us from our foes;

The Lord a-bove, in ten - der love, Hath sav'd us from our foes;

The Lord a-bove, in ten - der love, Hath sav'd us from our foes; Through

Through Wash-ing-ton the thing is done, The

Through

Through Wash-ing-ton the thing is done, The war is at a

Wash-ing-ton the thing is done, The war is at a close. The

THANKSGIVING HYMN

THE Lord above, in tender love,
Hath sav'd us from our foes;
Through Washington the thing is done,
The war is at a close.

America has won the day,
Through Washington, our chief;
Come let's rejoice with heart and voice,
And bid adieu to grief.

Now we have peace, and may increase
In number, wealth, and arts;
If every one, like Washington,
Will strive to do their parts.

Industry and frugality,
Will all our taxes pay;
In virtuous ways, we'll spend our days,
And for our rulers pray.

The Thirteen States, united sets,
In Congress simply grand;
The Lord himself preserve their health,
That they may rule the land,

Whilst every State, without its mate,
Doth rule itself by laws,
Will sovereign be, and always free;
To grieve there is no cause.

Then sure am I, true liberty
Of every sort will thrive;
With one accord we'll praise the Lord,
All glory to Him give.

National Songs

★★★★★★★★★★★★

A TOAST TO
WASHINGTON

THE occasion of this toast was probably one of two great celebrations in Philadelphia honoring President Washington, either during his passage through that city on April 20, 1789, on his way to taking the oath of office in New York, or on September 4, 1790, when the seat of government was in Philadelphia.[1] The author and composer, Francis Hopkinson, would certainly have been among the prominent citizens who planned the festivities for both occasions.

'Tis Wash-ing-ton's health, fill a bump-er a - round, For he is our glo - ry and pride. Our arms shall in bat-tle with con-quest be crowned Whilst vir-tue and he's on our side. Our arms shall in bat-tle with con-quest be crowned Whilst vir-tue and he's on our side - , and he's on our side.

'**T**IS Washington's health -- fill a bumper around,
For he is our glory and pride;
Our arms shall in battle with conquest be crowned,
Whilst virtue and he's on our side.

' Tis Washington's health -- loud cannons should roar,
And trumpets the truth should proclaim;
There cannot be found, search all the world o'er,
His equal in virtue and fame.

' Tis Washington's health -- our hero to bless,
May heaven look graciously down!
Oh! long may he live our hearts to possess,
And freedom still call him her own.

Adams & Liberty

THOMAS Paine composed the verses of this patriotic song for a concert of the Massachusetts Charitable Fire Society in Boston on June 1, 1798. The title pays tribute to John Adams, the second president of the United States. Paine set the words to the tune of a very popular, if somewhat ribald song, TO ANACREON IN HEAVEN, a tune with a glorious destiny. For a thorough discussion of the history of this tune, the reader is referred to Oscar Sonneck's excellent essay.[1]

Ye sons of Co-lum-bia who brave-ly have fought For those
May you long taste the bless-ings your val-or has bought And your

rights which un-stained from your sires have de-scend-ed.
sons reap the soil which your fa-thers de-fend-ed. 'Mid the

reign of mild peace May your na-tion in-crease with the glo-ry of

Rome and the wis-dom of Greece; And ne'er may the sons of Co-lum-bia be

slaves, While the earth bears a plant, or the sea rolls its waves.

YE sons of Columbia, who bravely have fought
For those rights which unstained from your sires have descended,
May you long taste the blessings your valour has bought
And your sons reap the soil which your fathers defended,
   Mid the reign of mild peace
   May your nation increas
With the Glory of Rome, and the wisdom of Greece;
And ne'er may the sons of Columbia be slaves,
While the earth bears a plant, or the sea rolls its waves.

In a clime whose rich vales feed the marts of the world
Whose shores are unshaken by Europe's commotion
The trident of Commerce should never be hurled,
To incense the legitimate powers of the ocean.
   But should pirates invade
   Though in thunder arrayed,
Let your cannon declare the free charter of Trade.
For ne'er shall the sons, &c.

While France her huge limbs bathes recumbent in blood,
And society's base threats with wide dissolution;
May Peace, like the dove who returned from the flood,
Find an ark of abode in our mild Constitution!
   But though peace is our aim,
   Yet the boon we disclaim
If bought by our Sovereignty, Justice or Fame,
For ne'er shall the sons, &c.

Let our patriots destroy Anarch's pestilent worm,
Lest our Liberty's growth should be checked by corrosion.
Then let clouds thicken round us, we heed not the storm,
Our realm fears no shock, but the earth's own explosion.
   Foes assail us in vain
   Though their fleets bridge the main,
For our altars and laws with our lives we'll maintain.
And ne'er shall the sons, &c.

PAUL JONES

Tune: TO ANACREON IN HEAVEN (see p.82)

AMONG the experienced sea-captains who offered their services to the newly-forming American Navy during the Revolution was the swashbuckling Scotsman, John Paul Jones. He prowled about the seas near the British Isles, capturing many English ships and diverting their cargo to the American rebels. His notorious exploits inspired the British epithet "the black Buccaneer", which the anonymous author of these verses has gracefully altered to "Liberty's Bold Buccaneer".

The first flag of the American Navy was raised by Jones on the **Alfred**; Esek Hopkins was the first commander of the American naval fleet. The **Richard** (or, the **Bonhomme Richard**) was the ship Jones commanded in the celebrated engagement of September 23, 1779, at Flamborough Head off the coast of Jones' native Scotland, which culminated in the capture of the British ship **Serapis**.

A song unto Liberty's brave Buccaneer,
Ever bright be the fame of the patriot Rover,
For our rights he first fought in his "black privateer",
And faced the proud foe ere our sea they crossed over.
In their channel and coast,
He scattered their host,
And proud Britain robbed of her sea-ruling boast,
And her rich merchants' barks shunned the ocean in fear
Of Paul Jones, fair Liberty's brave Buccaneer.

In the first fleet that sailed in defense of our land,
Paul Jones forward stood to defend freedom's arbor,
He led the bold **Alfred** at Hopkins' command,
And drove the fierce foeman from Providence harbor,
'Twas his hand that raised
The first flag that blazed,
And his deeds 'neath the "Pine Tree" all ocean amazed,
For hundreds of foes met a watery bier
From Paul Jones, fair Liberty's brave Buccaneer.

His arm crushed the Tory and mutinous crew
That strove to have freemen inhumanly butchered;
Remember his valor at proud Flamborough,
When he made the bold **Serapis** to strike to the **Richard**;
Oh! he robbed of their store
The vessels sent o'er
To feed all the Tories and foes on our shore,
He gave freemen the spoils and long may they revere
The name of fair Liberty's bold Buccaneer.

The *FEDERAL CONSTITUTION* And *LIBERTY* Forever

THE following "New Patriotic Song" was probably performed at one of many subscription concerts presented in New York by James Hewitt, the composer and publisher. The nationalistic flavor of the verses, by the American play-wright William Milns, is further emphasized by the opening tune of WASHINGTON'S MARCH and by the YANKEE DOODLE chorus. The music-sheet, published in 1798, states that the song was received "with great applause."

Po-ets may sing of their Hel-i-con streams, Their Gods and their He-roes and fab-u-lous dreams, Their Gods and their He - roes and fab - u-lous dreams. They ne'er sang a song half so grand so di-vine As the glo-ri-ous toast we Co-lum - bi-ans boast: The Fed'ral Consti tution, boys, and Lib-er-ty for-e-ver, The Fed'ral Con-sti-tu-tion, boys, and Lib-er-ty for-e-ver.

POETS may sing of their Helicon streams,
 Their Gods and their Heroes and fabulous dreams.
They ne' er sang a song half so grand so divine
As the glorious toast we Columbians boast,
The Federal Constitution boys and Liberty forever.

A free navigation, Commerce and Trade,
We'll seek for no foe, of no foe be afraid.
Our Frigates shall ride, our defense and our pride,
Our Tars guard our coast, and huzza to our toast,
The Federal Constitution, Trade and Commerce boys forever.

Adams, the man of our choice, guides the helm,
No tempest can harm us, no storm overwhelm;
Our sheet anchors serve, and our bark rides secure,
So here's to the toast we Columbians boast,
The Federal Constitution and the President forever.

Montgomery, Warren still live in our songs,
Like them our Young Heroes shall spurn our wrongs,
The world will admire the zeal and the fire
Which blaze in the toast we Columbians boast,
The Federal Constitution and its Advocates forever.

When an enemy threats, all party shall cease;
We bribe no intriguers to buy a mean peace.
Columbians will scorn friend or foe to suborn;
We'll ne'er stain the toast, which as freemen we boast,
The Federal Constitution and Integrity forever.

HAIL! COLUMBIA

THE song HAIL! COLUMBIA grew out of the critical post-war years, when the new American nation was nearly torn apart by a war between France and England, following the French Revolution. Opinion was bitterly divided as to which of the warring nations deserved America's support. Washington had urged a policy of neutrality.

The stated aim of Joseph Hopkinson, author of the verses, was "... to get up an American spirit which should be independent of... both belligerents, and look and feel exclusively for our honor and rights. No allusion is made to France or England. ...the song found favor with both parties, for both parties were American." [1] The verses are set to the tune of THE PRESIDENT'S MARCH, a composition by the German-American musician, Philip Phile. The complete song was first performed at a benefit concert in 1798.

The exact date and occasion for which the original PRESIDENT'S MARCH was composed are still disputed; for a detailed and scholarly discussion of the controversy the reader is referred to Oscar Sonneck's essay. [2]

Hail! Co-lum-bia, hap-py land, Hail! ye he-roes heav'n born band, Who fought and bled in Free-dom's cause -, Who fought and bled in Free-dom's cause -, and when the storm of war was gone En-joyed - the - peace your va-lor won. Let In-de-pend-ence

HAIL! Columbia happy land,
Hail! Ye heroes heaven born band.
Who fought and bled in freedom's cause
And when the storm of war was gone
Enjoyed the peace your valor won.
Let Independence be our boast
Ever mindful what it cost
Ever grateful for the prize
Let its altar reach the skies.
    Firm, united let us be
    Rallying round our Liberty
    As a band of brothers joined
    Peace and safety we shall find.

Immortal Patriots, rise once more
Defend your rights, defend your shore,
Let no rude foe with impious hand
Invade the shrine where sacred lies
The toil and blood, the well-earned prize.
While offering peace sincere and just
In heaven we place a manly trust
That truth and Justice will prevail
And every scheme of bondage fail
    Firm, united, &c.

Sound, sound the trump of fame,
Let Washington's great name
Ring through the world with loud applause;
Let every clime to Freedom dear
Listen with a joyful ear
With equal skill, with godlike power
He governs in the fearful hour
Of horrid war, or guides with ease
The happier times of honest peace.
    Firm, united, &c.

Behold the Chief who now commands
Once more to serve his Country stands;
The rock on which the storm will beat,
But armed in virtue firm and true
His hopes are fixed on heaven and you.
When hope was sinking in dismay
When glooms obscured Columbia's day
His steady mind from changes free
Resolved on Death or Liberty.
    Firm, united, &c.

ODE for
AMERICAN INDEPENDENCE

As a finale for this songbook, the following work is presented. Written only thirteen years after the signing of the Declaration of Independence, and six years after the truce with England, its dramatic poetry and grandiose style embody the spirit of naive optimism that characterized post-Revolutionary patriotic songs.

'Tis done! the e-dict pass'd, By heav'n - de - creed -, And Han - -cock's name con-firms the glo-rious deed. On this au-spi-cious morn Was In-de-pend-ence born. Pro-pi-tious day! Hail the U-nit-ed States of blest A-mer-i - ca.

Fly! Fly! Fly, swift-wing'd

Fly! Fly! Fly, swift-wing'd

Fame, the news , the news pro claim; From shore to

shore Let can nons roar And joy-ful voi ces shout Co lum-bia's

name, Shout, shout Co-lum-bia's name, Co lum bia's name.

'TIS done! the edict passed, by Heaven decreed
And Hancock's name confirms the glorious deed.
On this auspicious morn
Was Independence born.
Propitious day! Hail the United States of blest America.
  Fly! Fly! Fly, swift-wing'd Fame,
  The news, the news proclaim
  From shore to shore, let cannons roar,
  And joyful voices shout Columbia's name.

See haughty Britain, fending hosts of foes,
With vengeance armed, our freedom to oppose.
But Washington, the Great,
Dispelled impending fate,
And spurned each plan: Americans combine to hail the godlike man.
  Fly! Fly! &c.

Let Saratoga's crimson plains declare
The deeds of Gates, that "thunderbolt of war" :
His trophies graced the field
He made whole armies yield --
A veteran band: In vain did Burgoyne strive his valor to withstand.
  Fly! Fly! &c.

Pale terror marches on, with solemn stride;
Cornwallis trembles, Britain's boasted pride;
He and his armed hosts
Surrender all their posts
To Washington, the Friend of Liberty, Columbia's favorite son.
  Fly! Fly! &c.

Now shall the useful arts of peace prevail
And commerce flourish, favored by each gale;
Discord forever cease
Let Liberty and Peace
And Justice reign. For Washington protects the scientific train.
  Fly! Fly! &c.

SOURCES AND NOTES

(Complete references will be found in the Bibliography.)

Ballads

p.6, FOUR SONGS TO THE TUNE "HEARTS OF OAK"

Tune

Source: Benjamin West, Bickerstaff's Boston Almanac for 1769. "Plate 8th, the New and Favorite LIBERTY SONG, neatly engraved and set to MUSICK for the VOICE, to which are also added the words."
Composer: William Boyce.

The original "Hearts of Oak" was written as a setting for verses by David Garrick in his play Harlequin's Invasion (1759). West's publication of the popular LIBERTY SONG, set to the same tune, is one of the rare cases in which music was printed with the words of a Revolutionary ballad.

Verses

p.7, THE LIBERTY SONG

Source: "A New Song to the Tune of Hearts of Oak", Broadside, Philadelphia 1768.
Author: John Dickinson, a prominent statesman of the Revolution and author of Letters from a Farmer in Pennsylvania. In a letter to James Otis of Boston, Dickinson stated that Dr. Arthur Lee of Virginia had collaborated with him in writing the verses for the LIBERTY SONG (Moore, Songs and Ballads, p. 37).

p.9, A PARODY ON THE LIBERTY SONG

Source: Moore, Songs and Ballads, p.41 Quoted from the Boston Gazette, September 26, 1768.
Author: Anonymous.

p.10, A NEW LIBERTY SONG

Source: Moore, Songs and Ballads, p.103. 1775. No further source given by Moore.
Author: J. W. Hewlings.

p.11, A REFUGEE SONG

Source: Moore, Songs and Ballads, p. 253 Quoted from the Royal Gazette, New York, March 1779.
Author: "A Refugee".

p.12, A SONG TO THE SONS OF LIBERTY

Tune
COME JOLLY BACCHUS or THE GLORIOUS FIRST OF AUGUST

Source: Charles Coffey, The Devil to Pay (1731), Air X, p. 11.
Composer: Anonymous.

Earlier songs set to this tune are associated with the death of King Charles II in 1685 ("Charles of Sweden") or with the accession of King George I in 1714 ("Glorious First of August"). Coffey's verses, beginning "Come jolly Bacchus, god of wine", indicate "Charles of Sweden" as the tune.

Verses

Source: "A New Song, addressed to the Sons of Liberty", Broadside, Boston 1768.
Author: "A Son of Liberty"

Notes

1. A complete description of the day's festivities, including frequent sounding of cannon, speeches, music, processions and toasts, is given in the broadside entitled "Postscript to the Boston News-Letter, August 25, 1768". The events being commemorated, the Stamp Act Riots of August 14 and 26, 1765, were described in some detail by Governor Francis Bernard in proclamations issued on August 15 and 28, 1765, offering substantial rewards for the names of the instigators.

p. 14, FOUR SONGS TO THE TUNE "DERRY DOWN"

Tune

Source: Charles Coffey, The Beggar's Wedding, (1729), Act III, Air VI. Music on p. 10 of Appendix.
Composer: Anonymous.

The tune called "Derry Down" in sources of the Revolutionary period was an old English favorite among ballad tunes (see p. 2 of Introduction), more commonly known as "King John and the Abbot of Canterbury", or "A Cobbler There Was". Broadsides referring to the tune date back into the seventeenth century, but its origin is unknown.

Three of many songs set to "Derry Down" during the Revolution are presented in this group. No tune is indicated in the source for the fourth song, "The Public Spirit of the Women", but the verses fit the meter of the tune perfectly, and they have been included to represent the unique and important contributions to the war made by American women.

Verses

p. 15, CASTLE ISLAND SONG

Source: Moore, Songs and Ballads, p.51
Quoted from a broadside, 1770.
Author: Anonymous.

p. 16, A NEW SONG TO AN OLD TUNE

Source: Moore, Songs and Ballads, p.106.
1775. No further source given by Moore.
Author: Anonymous.

p. 17, THE PUBLIC SPIRIT OF THE WOMEN

Source: Moore, Songs and Ballads, p.206.
1778. No other source given by Moore.
Author: Anonymous.

p. 18, THE EPILOGUE

Source: Moore, Songs and Ballads, p.220.
Quoted from a ballad sheet printed in New York and Philadelphia in October of 1778.
Author: Anonymous.

p. 20, TEA PARTY SONG

Tune
HOSIER'S GHOST

Source: Joseph Ritson, Select Collection (1813) Vol.III, p. 300, Song LXIII
Composer: Anonymous

Earlier versions of this tune, called "How Happy are Young Lovers" or "The Distracted Sailor", are frequently associated with sailors and shipwrecks. The version to which the title "Hosier's Ghost" refers is a ballad about Admiral Edward Vernon of the British Navy, who captured the town of Puerto Bello in the West Indies, in 1739. It begins "As near Portobello lying, On the gently swelling flood", and tells of a visit to Admiral Vernon from the ghost of Admiral Francis Hosier, who had commanded a British fleet at Puerto Bello in 1726, with less successful results.

The same tune is in American Musical Miscellany (p.52), under the name "The Storm" or "Cease, Rude Boreas".

Verses

Source: Moore, Songs and Ballads, p. 57.
Quoted from the Pennsylvania Packet, December, 1773.
Author: Anonymous.

Notes

1.   Dan Lacey, The Meaning of the American Revolution, New York: New American Library of World Literature, 1964. p.114.

p.22, A SONG ON LIBERTY

Tune
THE BRITISH GRENADIERS

Source: Chappell, Ballad Literature (1859) Vol. I, p.152.
Composer: Anonymous.

The tune is derived from earlier ballads, "The London Apprentice" or "All you that love good fellows", and was adapted in the 18th century as the song of the British Grenadier Guards. Chappell, writing in 1859, says that the tune he gives is "from a copy about a hundred years old."

Verses

Sources: The Royal American Magazine
Boston, May, 1774, p.192.
and
The Massachusetts Spy
Boston, May 26, 1774, Last Leaf
Author: Attributed to Joseph Warren

The poem seems to be a variant of THE NEW MASSACHUSETTS LIBERTY SONG, published on a Boston broadside of 1770. (See Frontispiece. The broadside bears no printed date, but a hand-written parody on the back of the copy in the Library of Congress is dated April, 1770.) The altered verses of 1774, presented on p. 23 of this book, appeared in two different periodicals published by the

Boston printer, Isaiah Thomas. On July 7 of the same year, Thomas began to use the famous "Join or Die" cartoon in the heading of The Massachusetts Spy.

Another variant of the same poem is found in 19th century sources under the title FREE AMERICA, with authorship attributed to Joseph Warren (e.g. Duyckinck's Cyclopaedia of American Literature, Vol.I, p.443, 1855; Stedman and Hutchinson's Library of American Literature, Vol.III, p.256-7, 1888.) However, no author is mentioned in the eighteenth-century sources cited above.

p. 24, THE WHIG

Tune
POOR ROBIN'S MAGGOT

Source: John Gay, The Beggar's Opera (1728) (Variant of 2nd Edition.) Air XXI, p.29.
Composer: Anonymous.

Gay identifies this tune as "Would you have a young virgin," referring to earlier verses by Thomas D'Urfey which were set to the dance tune, "Poor Robin's Maggot." In later versions, the tune is sometimes called "When the heart of a man is depress't with care," after Gay's verses.

Verses

Source: Sargent, Loyalist Poetry, p.56 Quoted from Rivington's Gazeteer, January 26, 1775.
Author: Anonymous.

p. 26, THE BANKS OF THE DEE AND A PARODY

Tune
LANGOLEE

Source: American Musical Miscellany (1798), p.34.
Composer: Anonymous.

On p.80 of Songs and Ballads, Frank Moore quotes a letter from Robert Burns which discusses Tait's new song, "The Banks of the Dee." Burns identifies the tune as "Langolee, to slow time." A tune nearly identical to the one given here is found on p.142 of Irish Melodies of Thomas Moore, under the name "Dear Harp of My Country (Air: New Langolee)." The American source calls the tune "The Banks of the Dee."

Verses
p.26, THE BANKS OF THE DEE

Source: Moore, Songs and Ballads, p.78. Quoted from The Pennsylvania Ledger, 1775.
Author: John Tait.

p.28, A PARODY ON THE BANKS OF THE DEE

Source: Moore, Songs and Ballads, p.81 1775. No further source given by Moore.
Author: Attributed to Oliver Arnold.

p.29, JUNTO SONG

Tune
A-BEGGING WE WILL GO, or
THE DUSKY NIGHT RIDES DOWN THE SKY

Source: American Musical Miscellany (1798), p.23.
Composer: Anonymous.

There are at least two tunes with the title "A-Begging We Will Go" in the ballad literature. One, which is found mainly in seventeenth century sources, and sometimes called "The Jovial Beggars", does not fit the verse meter of "The Junto Song". A different tune called "A-Begging We Will Go" appeared in association with a song from Fielding's Don Quixote in England (1734), beginning "The dusky night rides down the sky" and with the chorus "A-hunting we will go". The Fielding song is included in American Musical Miscellany with a tune which perfectly fits "The Junto Song".

Verses

Source: Moore, Diary, p.134. Quoted from Holt's Journal, New York, September 7, 1775.
Author: Anonymous.

p.30, THE IRISHMAN'S EPISTLE TO THE OFFICERS AND TROOPS AT BOSTON

Tune
THE IRISH WASHERWOMAN

Source: Benjamin Carr, Federal Overture (1794), p.4.
Composer: Anonymous.

The source of the verses (see below)

does not indicate a tune, and it seems doubtful that they were conceived to be sung at all. The meter of the lines is adaptable to the rhythm of the Irish jig, but the six-line verse structure conflicts with the eight-line requirements of jig-tunes. It will also be noted that the third verse has only four lines. Nevertheless, the "Epistle" has been included in this book because of its charm and relevancy, and its famous pun on "Concord" and "discord".

Of the many jig tunes current in the colonies at the time of the Revolution, I have selected "The Irish Washerwoman" as a setting for these verses because it is included in the Federal Overture, a recognized source of popular tunes of the era. (J.A. Scott has coupled the verses with a slightly different version of the same tune, in his 1968 edition of Moore's Diary of the American Revolution, (Washington Square Press). Carr's version of the tune has been abridged here to accommodate the six-line verses. For performance, the last two lines of the first verse can be re-used effectively to complete the short third verse.

Verses

Source: Pennsylvania Magazine, May, 1775.
Author: "Paddy".

p. 32, THE KING'S OWN REGULARS

Tune
AN OLD COURTIER OF THE QUEEN'S

Source: Chappell, Ballad Literature (1859), p. 300.
Composer: Anonymous.

This popular ballad setting goes back to the early seventeenth century. It hardly has a tune at all, but a chant which conforms to the flexible rhythm of the verses, plus a chorus that is little more than a final cadence formula. The "music" of the different versions from eighteenth-century sources varies slightly in the length of the "chorus". The version presented by Chappell has one of the longest chorus sections.

Verses

Source: Moore, Diary, p. 214
Quoted from the Pennsylvania Evening Post, March 30, 1776.
Author: Anonymous.

Notes

1.   The Pennsylvania Evening Post, March 30, 1776, quoted in Moore's Diary, p. 213.
2.   Loc. cit.

p. 34, A NEW SONG, by Sir Peter Parker

Tune
COME, LET US PREPARE

Source: Charles Coffey, The Beggar's Wedding (1729), Air IV, Act II. Music, p. 7 of Appendix.
Composer: Anonymous.

As yet, I have found no tune with the title or first line "Well met, Brother Tar", which was indicated as the setting by the author of these verses. Of the various other tunes from the ballad-opera era that provide appropriate settings for the verse structure, "Come, let us prepare" was selected as the most suitable to the content.

Verses

Source: Moore, Songs and Ballads, p.135 "... written and printed in London", 1777.
Author: Anonymous.

p. 36, THE CONGRESS

Tune
NANCY DAWSON

Source: The Universal Magazine: London, October, 1760; p. 208.
Composer: Anonymous.

The tune is named for a popular dancer in the London theatre during the mid-eighteenth century. The original verses praise her beauty, grace and talent.

Verses

Source: Sargent, Loyalist Poetry, p. 70
Quoted from Towne's Evening Post, Spring of 1776.
Author: Anonymous.

p. 38, A WAR SONG

Tune
PORTSMOUTH

Source: The Dancing Master, 13th Edition, London: W. Pearson, 1707, p.243.

Composer: Anonymous.

As yet, I have found no other ballads from eighteenth-century sources written to this earlier dance tune. Chappell suggests that the name of Portsmouth, a port of embarcation for the British Navy, is naturally associated with departures and with farewells to loved ones (Ballad Literature, Vol. II, p. 605).

Verses

Source: Moore, Songs and Ballads, p. 115.
    Quoted from a songsheet, printed by Benjamin Dearborn, 1776.
Author: Attributed to Benjamin Dearborn.

p. 40, COLLINET AND PHEBE

Tune
AS JAMIE GAY BLITHE GANGED HIS WAY

Source: James Johnson, The Scots Musical Museum, 1787-1788. Vol. I, p. 15, no. 14.
Composer: Attributed to George Berg.

The strong similarity of this tune and the verse content to earlier songs, such as "Amoret and Phyllis", "Colin and Lucy", "Young Philoret and Celia Met", suggests that Berg arranged, rather than composed, the melody of "Jamie Gay" for a new set of verses. I have added the final two-measure extension from Ritson's version of "Amoret and Phillis" (Select Collection, Vol. III, p. 90) because it seems appropriate for this set of verses.

Verses

Source: The Pennsylvania Magazine, February 1776, p. 89.
Author: "Maryland".

p. 42, THE BATTLE OF TRENTON

Tune
FIRE OF LOVE

Source: Thomas D'Urfey, Pills to Purge Melancholy (1719-20), Vol. IV, p. 265.
Composer: R. King (See p. 381, Vol. 1, The London Stage, Van Lenner)

The original song, "The Fire of Love in Youthful Blood" was sung in Shadwell's play, The Amorous Bigotte in 1690. The tune has been adapted here as a setting for "The Battle of Trenton" in accordance with the suggestion in Moore (Songs and Ballads,

p. 150). Two half-measures have been deleted from the second part of the melody to accommodate the new verses.

Verses

Source: Moore, Songs and Ballads, p. 150 1776. Quoted from Rufus W. Griswold, Curiosities of American Literature.
Author: Anonymous.

p. 44, TWO SONGS TO THE TUNE "WAT'RY GOD"

Tune

Source: "The Wat'ry God. A celebrated song written on Lord Hawkes victory over Conflans in 1759". Songsheet. Dublin: John Lee, c. 1780. British Museum pressmark 1601. a. (102). (The tune and verses have been reproduced in this book with the kind permission of the British Museum Music Room.)
Composer: Anonymous.

There are two tunes associated with the verses beginning "The Wat'ry God great Neptune lay" by Mr. Wignel. The first tune was composed by John Worgan in 1759, the year of Lord Hawke's victory. Worgan's setting of Wignel's verses is entitled "Neptune's Resignation" (British Museum pressmark G. 312.(224)). The second tune, which is used in this book, is from a Dublin songsheet of c. 1780, entitled "The Wat'ry God". Irish interest in the song may be explained by the fact that Lord Hawke's mission in 1759 was to thwart France's planned invasion of Scotland and Ireland.

Verses

p. 45, A PARODY ON THE WAT'RY GOD

Source: Moore, Songs and Ballads, p. 156 1776. No further source given by Moore.
Author: Anonymous.

p. 47, A SONG ABOUT CHARLESTON

Source: Moore, Songs and Ballads, p. 293 Quoted from a ballad sheet of 1780.
Author: "An Officer of the Royal Army".

p.48,THE FATE OF JOHN BURGOYNE

Tune
THE WHITE COCKADE

Source: The Scots Musical Museum (1796), p.146.
Composer: Anonymous.

There is no indication of a tune with this ballad, but the regular meter of the verses suggests that it may have been sung to a popular military tune. "The White Cockade" was selected as an appropriate setting because it is often mentioned as a marching song of the Continental Army, and because it appears so frequently in American song collections published just after the Revolution.

Verses

Source: Moore, Songs and Ballads, p.185 1777. No further source given by Moore.
Author: Anonymous.

Notes

1. Quoted by Moore, Songs and Ballads,p.175. No further source is given by Moore.

2. Loc. cit.

p.50,THE REBELS

Tune
BLACK JOAK

Source: W.R. Chetwood, The Generous Freemason (1731), Air XI, p.20
Composer: Anonymous.

In slightly variant versions, this tune is included in several ballad operas under the names of "Black Joak", "Coal Black Joak" and "The Black Joke". The words set to this tune in The Generous Freemason ("Of all the girls in our town, That with two legs walk up and down") and in Coffey's Beggar's Wedding ("Of all the girls in our town, Or black, or yellow, or fair, or brown") are curiously similar to the words of the original song "Nancy Dawson" ("Of all the girls in our town, The black, the fair, the red, the brown"), which were set to an entirely different tune.(See p.36.)

Verses

Source: Moore, Songs and Ballads, p.196. Quoted from the Pennsylvania Ledger, 1778.
Author: Captain Smyth of Simcoe's Queen's Rangers.

p.53,THE BRITISH LIGHT INFANTRY

Tune
BLACK SLOVEN

Source: Universal Magazine; London, February, 1771, p.95.
Composer: Anonymous.

The adaptation of this hunting song as an emblem for a unit of foot soldiers seems surprising. The name of the tune comes from a favorite hunting-horse, as evidenced by the original verse:

Last Valentine's day when bright Phoebus shone clear,
I had not been hunting for more than a year; taleo, etc.
I mounted Black Sloven, o'er the road made him bound
For I heard the hounds challenge and the hornes sweetly sound. Taleo,etc.

In Olden Time Music (Boston: Ticknor, 1888, p.161), H.M. Brooks quotes a very similar tune from a manuscript sheet in the Essex Institute in Salem. It is labelled "Black Sloven" and accompanied by the following marginal note:"The tune played on Drum and Fife when Colonel Pickering's Regiment marched from Salem to Lexington, April 19, 1775".

Verses

Source: Moore, Songs and Ballads, p.204. Quoted from the Royal Gazette; New York, 1778.
Author: "A loyal American refugee".

p.54,THE HALCYON DAYS OF OLD ENGLAND

Tune
YE MEDLEY OF MORTALS

Source: "The Masquerade Song sung by Mr. Beard at Ranelagh", Songsheet in the British Museum, London, c.1750. (The tune has been used in this book with the kind permission of the British Museum Music Room.)
Composer: William Defesch.

The tune takes its name from the first line of "The Masquerade Song". It is a variant of several similar ballads which all share the distinctive chorus "Tantara ra ra, _____ all! _____ all!" The blank is supplied with words appropriate to the content of the song, and the chorus constitutes the punchline of the verse.

Verses

Source: Moore, Songs and Ballads, p. 200
Quoted from the London Evening Post, 1778.
Author: Attributed to Authur Lee.

p.57, THREE SONGS TO THE TUNE "YANKEE DOODLE"

Tune

Source: Benjamin Carr, The Federal Overture, p. 4.
Composer: Anonymous. Arranged by Benjamin Carr.

The variant of "Yankee Doodle" given here is the first version which appeared in print in America, according to Oscar Sonneck (Report, p. 121). The single surviving manuscript of the complete Federal Overture was brought to light after the essay by Sonneck was published; it was released for publication only recently. Therefore, the music of this version does not appear in the Sonneck essay, although he knew, through advertisements and theatre programs, that "Yankee Doodle" was one of the tunes in the Federal Overture.

Verses

p.58, THE BATTLE OF THE KEGS

Source: Moore, Songs and Ballads, p.209.1778.
No further source given by Moore.
Author: Francis Hopkinson.

p.60, YANKEE DOODLE'S EXPEDITION TO RHODE ISLAND

Source: Moore, Songs and Ballads, p. 231
Quoted from The Royal Gazette;
New York, October 1778.
Author: Anonymous.

p.61, THE RECESS

Source: Moore, Songs and Ballads, p. 278.
Quoted from a songsheet printed in America. The song was originally printed in England in 1779.
Author: "A true friend of the King and the Colonies."

Notes

1. Oscar Sonneck, Report on "The Star-Spangled Banner", "Hail Columbia", "America" and "Yankee Doodle", pp. 79-156.

p.62, THE AMERICAN VICAR OF BRAY

Tune
THE VICAR OF BRAY

Source: Joseph Ritson, Select Collection (1813), Vol. III, p.272.
Composer: Anonymous.

Verses
Source: Sargent, Loyalist Poetry, p. 94
Quoted from the Royal Gazette;
New York, June 30, 1779.
Author: Anonymous.

Notes

1. While recognizing that the story is historically unfounded (Ballad Literature, p. 787), Chappell quotes Fuller's traditional account of Simon Aleyn who was Vicar of Bray from 1540 to 1588:

He was a Papist under the reign of Henry VIII, and a Protestant under Edward VI; He was a Papist again under Mary, and once more became a Protestant in the reign of Elizabeth. When this scandal to the gown was reproached for his versatility of religious creeds, and taxed for being a turncoat and an inconstant changeling...he replied, "Not so neither; for if I changed my religion, I am sure I kept true to my principle; which is to live and die the Vicar of Bray." (Ballad Literature, p. 652).

C.M. Simpson says, "The search for a historical original has proved fruitless, especially the attempt to connect the turncoat with Simon Aleyn, a sixteenth-century holder of the office." (British Broadside Ballad, p. 736).

2. The true identity of the American Vicar of Bray is not known. Sargent says, "The subject of this piece is said to be Dr. William Smith of Philadelphia; but, if so, many of the hits are untrue as well as ill-natured". (Loyalist Poetry, p. 94). A more likely candidate would seem to be Benjamin Towne, publisher of the Pennsylvania Evening Post. His newspaper flourished before, during and after the British occupation of Philadelphia by espousing the viewpoint of any political faction in power. After the truce, when

business fell off, Towne asked for help from a former supporter, John Witherspoon, then an influential member of Congress. Witherspoon wrote for Towne an insulting and abject recantation, with a justification similar to the one attributed to Simon Aleyn, and promised to help Towne if he would sign and publish it. Towne refused, but Witherspoon published the document, anyhow, under Towne's name.(See Isaiah Thomas, History of American Printing, Vol.I, pp. 410-14, Appendix H^B.)

p.64,AN APPEAL TO LOYALISTS

Tune
THE CUTPURSE, or PACKINGTON'S POUND

Source: John Hippisley, A Sequel to the Opera Flora (1733), Air XIV, p. 28. Music, p. 7 of Appendix.
Composer: Anonymous.

"Packington's Pound" is one of the oldest and most frequently used ballad tunes. Its association with the title "The Cutpurse" comes from the verses set to this tune by Ben Jonson for his comedy Bartholomew Fair, revived in 1682.

Verses

Source: Moore, Songs and Ballads, p. 289. 1780. No further source given by Moore.
Author: Anonymous.

p.66,CORNWALLIS BURGOYNED

Tune
MAGGIE LAUDER

Source: Charles Coffey, The Beggar's Wedding (1729). Act I, Air VI, p. 20.
Composer: Anonymous.

The lively Scotch tune, "Maggie Lauder", was frequently used by the English ballad-opera writers. Coffey identifies the tune given here as "Moggy Lawther on a day". A set of variations on "Maggie Lauder", arranged for the harpsichord by Alexander Reinagle and printed in Philadelphia in 1787, indicates that the tune known in the colonies was essentially the same as the earlier one.

Verses
Source: Moore, Songs and Ballads, p. 367. No further source given by Moore.
Author: Anonymous.

Hymns

p.70,CHESTER

Source: William Billings, The New England Psalm Singer, (1770), p. 91.
Music and Verses were composed by Billings.

p.72,BUNKER HILL

Music

Source: Andrew Law, The Rudiments of Music, 4th Edition, (1792) p. 68.
Composer: Attributed to Andrew Law.

Verses
Source: "The American Hero. Made on the Battle of Bunker Hill and the Burning of Charlestown". Broadside, Boston (1775?).
Author: Nathaniel Niles.

p.74,ODE FOR THE FOURTH OF JULY

Source of Music and Verses:
American Musical Miscellany, (1798), p. 130.

Neither the author of the verses nor the arranger of the hymn setting is identified in the source. Possible origins of the tune "God Save the King", which is the melody of this hymn, are explored at length by Chappell in Ballad Literature, pp. 691-707. Oscar Sonneck discusses the relationship of the British national anthem to American national songs in his Report on...America..., pp. 73-78.

p.76,THANKSGIVING HYMN

Music

Source: Oliver Brownson, Select Harmony, (1783), p. 17, "Kettery".

This lovely fuging-tune is a setting for "The Lord's Prayer" in Brownson's collection, which was published the year of the truce between England and America. Brownson does not indicate the name of the composer.

Verses

Source: Moore,Songs and Ballads,p. 376.1783. No further source given by Moore.
Author: Anonymous.

National Songs

p.80, A TOAST TO WASHINGTON

Source: "Brother Soldiers All Hail, a Favorite New Patriotic Song in Honor of Washington to which is added A Toast, written and composed by Francis Hopkinson, Esq." Songsheet, Philadelphia: Carr, 1794.

Notes

1. Sonneck, Report on...Hail Columbia..., p. 57, quotes contemporary newspaper accounts of both celebrations, in which toasts played an important part.

p.82, ADAMS AND LIBERTY

Tune
TO ANACREON IN HEAVEN

Source: American Musical Miscellany, (1798), p. 211.
Composer: John Stafford Smith.

The original song, "To Anacreon in Heaven" was composed as the official anthem of an English musical organization, The Anacreontic Society. The words, by Ralph Tomlinson, Esq., reiterate with each verse the purpose of the members, which was to entwine "The myrtle of Venus with Bacchus' wine". Although the society dissolved in the early 1790's, the tune became a great favorite as a setting for new verses, both in England and the United States.

Verses

Source: American Musical Miscellany, (1798), pp. 211-218.
Author: Robert Treat (scil. Thomas) Paine.

Notes

1. Sonneck, Report, pp. 17-28.

p.84, PAUL JONES

Tune
TO ANACREON IN HEAVEN (See ADAMS AND LIBERTY)

Verses

Source: Neeser, American Naval Songs, (1938), p.24.
Author: Anonymous.

The Neeser collection gives no source for this song, nor does it indicate a tune. The flavor of the verses suggests that they were written toward the end of the eighteenth century, when so many American Revolutionary War heroes were glorified in song. The particular form of the verses indicates "To Anacreon in Heaven" as the most likely tune to which the song was set. (The only other ballad tune I have found to fit this unusual verse structure is "Packington's Pound". See p. 64.)

p.86, THE FEDERAL CONSTITUTION AND LIBERTY FOREVER

Source: "The Federal Constitution and Liberty Forever, A New Patriotic Song by Mr. Milns...".
Songsheet, New York: James Hewitt for B. Carr, 1798.
Composer: "Music adapted by Mr. Hewitt".
Author of Verses: William Milns.

The music is an arrangement of two patriotic tunes. It opens with the melody of "Washington's March", and the chorus is set to "Yankee Doodle", with a bridging section presumably composed by James Hewitt.

The identification of the first tune as "Washington's March", or "Washington's March at the Battle of Trenton", as distinct from the tune of "The New President's March", is clarified by William Treat Upton in his 1964 revision of Oscar Sonneck's Bibliography of American Secular Music, Eighteenth Century, pp. 450-452.

p.88, HAIL! COLUMBIA

Source: "The President's March. A New Federal Song." Songsheet, Philadelphia: Willig, 1798.
Composer: Phillip Phile.
Author of Verses: Joseph Hopkinson.

Notes

1. Sonneck, Report on...Hail Columbia..., p. 43. Quoted from a letter written by Joseph Hopkinson to Rev. Rufus W. Griswold on August 24, 1840.

2. Op. Cit. pp. 43-72.

p. 90, ODE FOR AMERICAN INDEPENDENCE

Source: The Massachusetts Magazine; July,
1789; p. 453.

Composer: Horatio Garnet.
Author of Verses: Daniel George.

BIBLIOGRAPHY

Aitken, John (Editor). The Scots Musical Museum. Philadelphia: Aitken, 1797. (Evans No. 31701).

"The American Hero. Made on the Battle of Bunker Hill and the Burning of Charlestown". Broadside, Boston (1775?) (Evans No. 14349).

American Musical Miscellany. Northampton, Massachusetts: Andrew Wright for Daniel Wright, 1798. (Evans No. 33294).

Ashley, Maurice. Great Britain to 1688. Ann Arbor: University of Michigan Press, 1961.

Berger, Arthur V. "The Beggar's Opera, The Burlesque and Italian Opera". Music and Letters, XVII, April 1936, p. 93.

Bernard, Governor Francis. "A Proclamation". Boston, August 15, 1765, (Evans No. 41563); and August 28, 1765 (Evans No. 41562).

Billings, William. The New England Psalm Singer. Boston: Edes and Gill, 1770. (Evans No. 11572).

"Black Sloven. A New Song." The Universal Magazine of Knowledge and Pleasure, Vol. XLVIII, February 1771, p.95.

Bronson, Bertrand Harris. The Ballad as Song. Berkeley and Los Angeles: University of California Press, 1969.

Brooks, Henry Mason (Compiler). Olden-Time Music. Boston: Ticknor and Company, 1888. (Library of American Civilization No. 15842).

"Brother Soldiers All Hail, a Favorite New Patriotic Song to which is added A Toast, written and composed by Francis Hopkinson, Esq." Songsheet. Philadelphia: Carr, 1794. (Evans No. 35637).

Brownson, Oliver. Select Harmony. New Haven: Brownson, 1783. (Evans No. 17857).

Carr, Benjamin, "The Federal Overture" (First published Philadelphia: Carr, 1794) Facsimile Edition in Irving Lowens, Benjamin Carr's Federal Overture. 1794. Philadelphia: Musical Americana, 1957.

Chappell, William. The Ballad Literature and Popular Music of the Olden Time. London: Chappell and Company, 1859.

Chappell, William. The Ballad Literature and Popular Music of the Olden Time. Reprint of the 1859 Edition with new Introduction by Frederick W. Sternfeld. 2 Vols. New York: Dover, 1965.

Chetwood, William Rufus. The Generous Freemason. London: J. Roberts, 1731.

Clowes, Sir William Laird. The Royal Navy. A History. 5 Vols. (First published London: Sampson Low, Marston and Company, 1898) Reprint of 1898 Edition, New York: AMS Press, Inc., 1966.

Coffey, Charles. The Beggar's Wedding. London: James and John Knapton, 1729.

Coffey, Charles. The Devil to Pay. London: J. Watts, 1731.

"A New Song. Tune, As Jamie Gay Blithe Gang'd his Way". The Pennsylvania Magazine, February 1776, p.89.

Commager, Henry Steele and Richard B. Morris. The Spirit of '76. 2 Vols. New York: Bobbs-Merrill, 1958.

The Dancing Master. 13th Edition. London: W. Pearson, 1707.

D'Urfey, Thomas. Wit and Mirth, Pills to Purge Melancholy. 6 Vols. London: W. Pearson for J. Tonson, 1719-20.

Duyckink, Evart A. and George L. Cyclopaedia of American Literature. New York: Scribner, 1855.

"The Federal Constitution and Liberty Forever. A New Patriotic Song by Mr. Milns". Songsheet. New York: Hewitt for Carr, 1798. (Evans No. 34113).

Gay, John. The Beggar's Opera. Variant of 2nd Edition. London: J. Watts, 1728.

Hippisley, John. A Sequel to the Opera of Flora. London: A. Bettesworth and C. Hitch et al., 1732.

Hopkinson, Francis. "A Toast" (See "Brother Soldiers All Hail ...")

"The Irishman's Epistle to the Officers and Troops at Boston". The Pennsylvania Magazine, February 1775, p. 232.

Johnson, James (Compiler). Scots Musical Museum. 2 Vols. Edinburgh: J. Johnson 1787-88.

Kobre, Sidney. The Development of the Colonial Newspaper. Gloucester, Mass.: Peter Smith, 1960.

Law, Andrew. The Rudiments of Music. 4th Edition. Cheshire, Ct.: William Law, 1792. (Evans No. 24466).

Lowens, Irving. Benjamin Carr's "Federal Overture" (1794). Philadelphia: Musical Americana. 1957.

"The Masquerade Song sung by Mr. Beard at Ranelagh". Songsheet. London: c. 1780. (British Museum pressmark G. 305 (174)).

McDonald, Forrest. "Introduction" in Empire and Nation. Englewood Cliffs, N.J.: Prentice-Hall, 1962.

Moore, Frank (Compiler). The Diary of the Revolution. A Centennial Volume. Hartford: J.B. Burr, 1876.

Moore, Frank (Compiler). <u>The Diary of the American Revolution:</u> <u>1775-1781</u>. Abridged, Edited, and with an introduction by John Anthony Scott. New York: Washington Square Press, 1968.

Moore, Frank. <u>Songs and Ballads of the American Revolution</u>. New York: D. Appleton, 1856. (Library of American Civilization No. 11349)

Moore, Frank. <u>Songs and Ballads of the American Revolution</u>. (Reprint of 1856 Edition.) Port Washington, New York; Kennikat Press, Inc., 1964.

Moore, Thomas (Poet and Compiler) <u>Irish Melodies</u>, the original airs restored and arrangements for the voice with pianoforte accompaniment by Charles Villiers Stanford. London: Boosey, 1895. Reprinted in London and New York: Boosey and Hawkes, 1940.

Moore, Warren. <u>Weapons of the American Revolution</u>. New York: Funk and Wagnalls, 1967.

"Nancy Dawson. A New Song". <u>The Universal Magazine of Knowledge</u> and Pleasure, Vol. XXVII, October 1760, p. 208.

Neeser, Robert W. <u>American Naval Songs and Ballads</u>. New Haven: Yale University Press, 1938.

Neumann, George C. <u>The History of Weapons of the American Revolution</u>. New York: Harper and Row, 1967.

"The New Massachusetts Liberty Song". Broadside. Boston, 1770. (Evans No. 42135).

"A New Song, addressed to the Sons of Liberty". Broadside. Boston, 1768. (Evans No. 41853).

"A New Song to the Tune Hearts of Oak". Broadside, Philadelphia, 1768. (Evans No. 10880).

Niles, Nathaniel. "The American Hero. A Sapphick Ode". Broadside. Norwich, Connecticut, October 1775. (Evans No. 14139).

"Postscript to the Boston News-letter". Broadside. Boston, August 25, 1768. (Evans No. 41866).

"The Presidents March. A New Federal Song". Songsheet. Philadelphia: Willig, 1798. (Evans No. 33902).

Reinagle, Alexander. <u>A Select Collection of the Most Favorite Scots Tunes</u>. Philadelphia: Dobson and Young, 1787. (Evans No. 20674).

Ritson, Joseph. <u>A Select Collection of English Songs</u>. 3 Vols. London: F.C. and J. Rivington, et al., 1813.

Sabine, Lorenzo. <u>Biographical Sketches of Loyalists of the American Revolution</u>. Port Washington, N.Y.: Kennikat Press, 1966. (Reprint of 1864 edition).

Sargent, Winthrop. <u>Loyalist Poetry of the Revolution</u>. Philadelphia: Collins, 1857. (Library of American Civilization No. 12065).

Simpson, Claude M. The British Broadside Ballad and Its Music. New Brunswick, N.J.: Rutgers University Press, 1966.

"A Song on Liberty to the Tune of the British Grenadier". The Royal American Magazine, May 1774, p. 192.

Sonneck, Oscar George Theodore. Report on "The Star Spangled Banner". "Hail Columbia", "America" and "Yankee Doodle". (First published by the Library of Congress in 1909) New York: Dover, 1972. (Reprint of 1909 edition.)

Stedman, Edmund Clarence and Ellen Mackay Hutchinson. Library of American Literature. 11 Vols. New York: C. L. Webster, 1888-90. (Library of American Civilization No. 21051).

Thomas, Isaiah. The History of American Printing. 2 Vols. Albany, N.Y.: J. Munsell, 1874. (Library of American Civilization No. 20054-5.)

Van Lennep, William (Editor) The London Stage 1660-1800. Carbondale, Ill.: Southern Illinois University Press, 1965.

Vickers, Kenneth H. England in the Later Middle Ages. London: Methuen and Company, 1961. (First published in 1913).

"The Wat'ry God. A celebrated Song written on Lord Hawkes victory over Conflans in 1759". Dublin: John Lee, c. 1780. (British Museum pressmark H. 1601.a. (102).)

West, Benjamin. Bickerstaff's Boston Almanac for 1769. 2nd Edition. Boston: Mein and Fleeming, 1768. (Evans No. 41898).

Winstock, Lewis. Songs and Music of the Redcoats. Harrisburg, Pa.: Stackpole Books, 1970.

BIBLIOGRAPHIES AND COLLECTIONS

Bristol, Roger P. Supplement to Charles Evans' American Bibliography. Charlottesville, Va.: University Press of Virginia, 1970.

Day, Cyrus Lawrence and Eleanor Boswell Murrie. English Song-Books 1651-1702. London: Oxford University Press, 1940.

Evans, Charles. American Bibliography. A Chronological Dictionary of all Books, Pamphlets and Periodical Publications printed in the United States of America from the genesis of printing in 1639 down to and including the year 1820. 12 Vols. Worcester, Massachusetts: American Antiquarian Society, 1903-1934. Reprinted in 1941-42 by Peter Smith, New York. Vol. 13 edited by Clifford K. Shipton; American Antiquarian Society, 1955; reprinted in 1962 by Peter Smith. Vol. 14, see Bristol.

Ford, Worthington Chauncey. Broadsides, Ballads, Etc. Printed in Massachusetts 1639-1800. Boston: Massachusetts Historical Society, 1922.

Hixon, Donald L. Music in Early America. A Bibliography of Music in Evans. Metuchen, N.J.: Scarecrow Press, 1970.

The Microbook Library of American Civilization. Chicago: Library Resources, Inc., 1972.

Shipton, Clifford K. (Editor) Early American Imprints 1639-1800. Worcester, Mass.: American Antiquarian Society, 1959. (Microcard reproductions of all existing items in the Evans Bibliography)

Sonneck, Oscar. Bibliography of Early American Secular Music, 18th Century. Revised and enlarged by William Treat Upton. New York: DaCapo Press, 1964.

Squire, William Barclay. Catalogue of Printed Music Published between 1487 and 1800 now in the British Museum. 2 Vols. Nendeln/Liechtenstein: Kraus Reprint, 1968.

Squire, William Barclay. "An Index of Tunes in the Ballad Operas", in The Musical Antiquary Vol.II, October 1910, pp. 1- 17.

University Microfilm Series-American Periodicals, 18th Century. Ann Arbor: University Microfilms.

Winslow, Ola Elizabeth. American Broadside Verse. New Haven: Yale University Press, MDCCCCXXX

Wolfe, Richard J. Secular Music in America 1801-1820. New York Public Library, 1964.

INDEX